Buckle Down™

Georgia Reading

Level 3

This book belongs to: ______________________________

Helping your schoolhouse meet the standards of the statehouse™

Acknowledgments

Illustration of the Montgolfier brothers' balloon flight before the royal family at Versailles, France, 1783, is reprinted courtesy of the Library of Congress, Prints and Photographs Division, LC-DIG-ppmsca-02472.

Six definitions and the pronunciation key from *Scott, Foresman Beginning Dictionary.* Copyright © 1976 by Scott, Foresman and Company. Reprinted by permission of Pearson Education, Inc.

Photograph of Pony Express rider Frank E. Webner, circa 1861, reprinted courtesy of the National Archives and Records Administration, Still Picture Branch, NWDNS-30-N-49-426.

Photograph of Eleanor Roosevelt, 1933. Reprinted courtesy of the Library of Congress, Prints and Photographs Division, LC-USZ62-25812.

Portrait of Ludwig von Beethoven, from a reproduction of a painting by Carl Jaeger, is reprinted courtesy of the Library of Congress, Prints and Photographs Division, LC-USZ62-29499.

"The Elves and the Shoemaker" by Jakob and Wilhelm Grimm, adapted for the stage by Mike Acton.

Excerpt from "The Star" from *Rhymes for the Nursery* by Ann and Jane Taylor. Public domain.

"Clouds" by Christina G. Rossetti. Public domain.

Illustration depicting Snow White and the Seven Dwarfs by Jessie Willcox Smith, from *A Child's Book of Stories* by Penrhyn W. Coussens, 1911. Public domain.

"Turkey Girl" by Red Gomez, based on a Zuni Indian folktale.

"Maha and the Little Red Fish" by Jill Foley, based on an Iraqi folktale.

Every effort has been made by the publisher to locate each owner of the copyrighted material reprinted in this publication and to secure the necessary permissions. If there are any questions regarding the use of these materials, the publisher will take appropriate corrective measures to acknowledge ownership in future publications.

ISBN 0-7836-4227-X

Catalog #1BDGA03RD01

2 3 4 5 6 7 8 9 10

Senior Editor: Melissa Brown, Ph.D; Project Editor: Mike Acton; Editors: Rick Zollo, Molly Minturn; Production Editor: Michael Hankes; Production Director: Jennifer Booth; Art Director: Chris Wolf; Graphic Designer: Erin Luong; Composition: Wyndham Books.

TABLE OF CONTENTS

Introduction

Do you like to read? If you do, reading is probably easy for you. You'll have fun reading the selections in this book. If you don't like to read, it may be because reading is difficult for you.

If reading isn't as easy as you'd like it to be, don't give up! If you're willing to practice, you can count on becoming a better reader than you are today. *Buckle Down Georgia Reading, Level 3,* will give you a lot of reading practice to help you read the best you can.

This workbook also has tips to help you become a better reader. Each lesson teaches a reading skill. These tips and lessons will help you to do your best on the Georgia state reading test, too.

So, go ahead, exercise your mind by working through this book. The more you practice reading, the better you'll get. And the better you get, the more fun you'll have doing it. Pretty soon, you'll be able to say, "I really like to read!"

How to Use This Workbook

In this *Buckle Down* workbook, you'll find several reading passages. Some of them are made-up stories (**fiction**), or **poems**. Others are about real things and real people (**nonfiction**).

Most lessons begin with a passage that will help you understand the tips that follow. These passages will give you reading practice that is fun.

The reading practice you do now will help you when you take the Georgia state reading test. But *more* important, it will help you be a better reader for the rest of your life.

Tips for Taking Reading Tests

Here are some very basic tips to help you do your best on any reading test. Throughout the workbook, you will find information that fully explains these basic tips.

TIP 1: Read the entire selection.

This is the *most* important thing you can do. If you don't read the selection, you won't know what it says. And if you don't know what it says, you can't hope to answer the questions correctly.

TIP 2: Keep moving through to the end.

Even if a word or an idea is difficult, don't stop reading. Keep your eyes moving (and your brain thinking) all the way to the end of the passage. This will help you get the big picture of what the selection is about.

Reading through to the end can also help you understand any new words or difficult ideas. Words that you already know can help you figure out words that you don't know.

TIP 3: Read the questions and answer choices carefully.

Don't be in a hurry. If you rush through a test, you're bound to make mistakes. If you take your time, you'll do your best work. Be sure to keep reading and thinking, though. This isn't the time to daydream about your next birthday party or what you'll do at recess.

TIP 4: Answer every question, even if you have to guess.

The only way to get a correct answer is to *answer the question.* If you don't try, you can't possibly get it right. If you do your best to answer a question—even a hard question—you just might get the right answer. On multiple-choice questions, try to find answers that you know are wrong, then guess from those that are left. You have nothing to lose by trying!

TIP 5: Choose the best answer to the question.

Several of the answer choices may look good, but one will always be better than the rest. Make sure your choice is the best answer to the question being asked. Words such as ***best***, ***most***, and ***least*** in a test question are reminders that you should look for the strongest choice among those listed.

The best tip of all

TIP 6: Have fun.

Relax. Of all the kinds of tests you'll ever have to take, reading just might be the most fun. For one thing, the passages are often interesting. So, read with the idea that you're going to enjoy yourself. You'll have a better time taking the test, and you'll probably do much better on it, too.

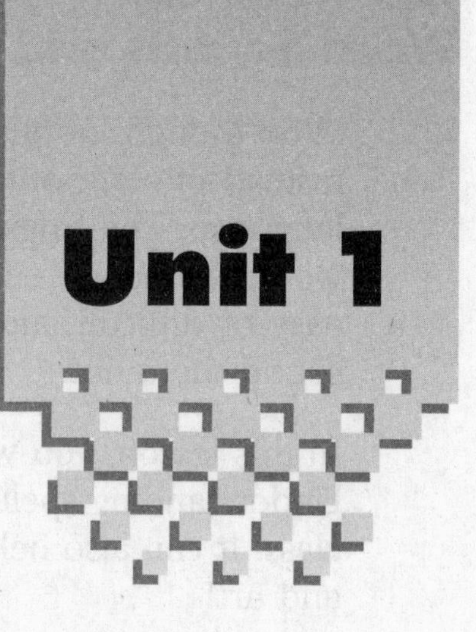

Words and Word Power

Before you could read, letters probably looked like a secret code. Later, you learned that code when you found that each letter makes its own special sound (or sounds). You sounded out letters as you read them aloud.

As you put sounds together, you made words. Reading aloud helped you decode unknown words easily and correctly. Then as reading became easier for you, you concentrated less on sounding out words and more on the meaning of the words you read. In time, you were able to read stories with feeling, so that the story was interesting to those listening.

Now, you must learn to gather clues about unknown words from the story. After you have gathered enough information, you will begin to understand what those unknown words mean.

In this unit, you will learn to search for clues as you try to figure out a word. If you practice using these clues, you will become a better reader.

In This Unit

- Word Sounds and Patterns
- Understanding New Words
- Word Power
- Finding New Words

Lesson 1

Word Sounds and Patterns

Who thought of putting a *c* in *place* instead of an *s*, or a *g* in *gem* instead of a *j*? Sometimes it might seem that there are no rules to our language. The English language has thousands and thousands of words. Some are easy to read. Others take a while to figure out. But easy or difficult, most English words follow rules that can help you sound them out.

In this lesson, you will learn some common word patterns. Understanding spelling patterns will help you a lot in your reading class. It can also help you in science, math, social studies—even music and art!

TIP 1: Separate words into sounds or syllables.

Separate difficult words into sounds. The sounds that make up a word can come from one letter or several letters. An example of a one-letter sound might be the **consonant** *l* (luh) or the **vowel** *a* in *lake*. Look at the following examples of words that have been separated into sounds:

pal   p / a / l   cut   c / u / t

The following are examples of how more than one letter can form a single sound:

thought   th / ough / t   weight   w / eigh / t

A **syllable** is a part of a word pronounced as one sound. Syllables can be vowels or vowels with consonants. Here are some examples of words broken into syllables:

climb / er   syl / la / ble

hos / pi / tal   wrin / kle

Circle the correct answers to Numbers 1 through 3.

1. How many syllables does the word *cat* have?
   A. 1
   B. 2
   C. 3
   D. 4

2. How many syllables does the word *because* have?
   A. 1
   B. 2
   C. 3
   D. 4

3. How many syllables does the word *basketball* have?
   A. 1
   B. 2
   C. 3
   D. 4

TIP 2: Some consonants can make either a hard sound or a soft sound.

C can make a hard "kuh" sound (*cat*) or a soft "suh" sound (*cent*).

G can make a hard "guh" sound (*girl*) or a soft "juh" sound (*gentle*).

But how do you know which sound is correct?

Try reading the word using each sound. See which sound makes the most sense in the word. (To get really good at this, you have to practice. The more you read, the easier this will become.)

Circle the correct answers to Numbers 4 through 7.

Mary bought her friend a <u>soda</u>.

4. Which word begins with the same sound as *soda*?
   A. cool
   B. child
   C. color
   D. circus

Simone's kitten has soft <u>golden</u> fur.

5. Which word begins with the same sound as *golden*?
   A. gym
   B. goose
   C. gentle
   D. giant

You will need a <u>key</u> to open that door.

6. Which word begins with the same sound as *key*?
   A. city
   B. cent
   C. cellar
   D. candle

When Jack climbed the beanstalk, he found the home of a <u>giant</u>.

7. Which word begins with the same sound as *giant*?
   A. gate
   B. game
   C. giraffe
   D. glasses

TIP 3: Consonants that stand together often combine their sounds.

When two consonants stand together in a word, they sometimes blend both letter sounds. For example, in the word ***plate***, you hear both the "puh" sound of ***p*** and the "luh" sound of ***l***. In ***crook***, you hear the "kuh" of ***c*** and the "ruh" of ***r***.

But other consonant groups, like *ch* in *por**ch***, make a completely new sound. Some consonant groups that make new sounds are *ch* ("chuh"), *sh* ("shuh"), *th* ("thuh"), *tch* ("chuh"), and *ph* ("fuh").

Look at the following words. If the **bold** letters blend their sounds together, circle *Blend*. If the bold letters make a brand new sound, circle *New Sound*.

8. i**tch** Blend New Sound

9. po**st** Blend New Sound

10. sti**nk** Blend New Sound

11. **ch**oice Blend New Sound

Circle the correct answers to Numbers 12 through 15.

The hillside was dotted with fluffy white sheep.

12. Which word begins with the same sound as *sheep*?
   A. such
   B. clip
   C. swat
   D. sharp

Black smoke poured out of the chimney.

13. Which word begins with the same sound as *chimney*?
   A. chop
   B. clear
   C. clip
   D. cattle

The phone rang as we walked into the house.

14. Which word begins with the same sound as *phone*?
    A. pants
    B. plane
    C. funny
    D. piano

I love to watch the stars on a summer evening.

15. Which word begins with the same sound as *stars*?
    A. stairway
    B. squirrel
    C. share
    D. spoken

TIP 4: When a vowel is followed by an *r*, the *r* controls the vowel's sound.

A vowel can make a long sound (its alphabet name) and a short sound (any vowel sound other than its alphabet name). But when placed together with the letter *r*, each vowel also makes another special sound. Each of these words has an *r*-controlled vowel sound:

b**ar**n B**er**t b**ir**d c**or**ner c**ur**l

Notice that *er*, *ir*, and *ur* sound alike. *Ar* and *or* make other sounds.

Remember, to control a vowel's sound, the *r* must come *after* the vowel.

Write the missing *r*-controlled vowel in each of the following sentences.

16. I went to visit Grandmother and Grandfather on their f___rm.

17. Grandfather asked me to help feed his h___rd of cows.

18. He showed me how to give the cows some hay with a big pitchf___rk.

19. When it was my t___rn, the cows got a big surprise.

20. I fed them some hay and a pack of bubble gum from my sh___rt pocket.

TIP 5: When a vowel is followed by one or more consonants (except *r*), it usually has a short-vowel sound.

The words below follow this rule:

band get ill not up

21. Think of two more words that follow this rule. Write them on the lines below.

____

____

TIP 6: When a vowel is followed by one consonant and then a final e, it usually has a long-vowel sound. The e at the end is silent.

Think of this vowel-consonant-*e* group as a train. The vowel is the engine. The consonant is the railcar. And the final *e* is the caboose.

Vowel Consonant Silent *e*

The following words are examples of this rule:

game Pete hike hope rule

TIP 7: When a vowel is followed by two consonants and a final e, it usually has a short-vowel sound. The final e is silent.

The following words are examples of this rule:

lance ledge bridge chance fudge

Complete the following sentences with a word from the box that follows. If the vowel sound of the word is short, circle Short. If it is long, circle Long. The first one is done for you.

lake	edge	twelve	like	dance

22. Cinderella went to the ball to ___dance___ with the prince. — (Short) / Long

23. She did not ____________ her mean stepsisters. — Short / Long

24. She stood near the ____________ of the dance floor until midnight. — Short / Long

25. As the clock struck ____________, the prince's horse trotted up the road. — Short / Long

26. The prince, however, had fallen off his horse into a ____________. — Short / Long

TIP 8: Usually, when two vowels stand together, the first vowel has a long sound and the second one is silent.

Many people remember this rule by learning this little poem:

When two vowels go walking,
The first one does the talking.

The following words are examples of this rule:

b**ai**t s**ea**w**ee**d l**ie** g**oa**lk**ee**per th**ou**gh st**ai**n

Complete the following sentences with the double-vowel words from the box that follows.

coat	keep	treat	rain

27. I wanted to go to the candy store to buy myself a __________.

28. The sky looked as if it might start to __________.

29. Mom wanted me to wear boots to __________ my socks dry.

30. I couldn't find my boots, so I removed my socks and put them in my __________ pocket!

TIP 9: Single vowels (except *a*) at the end of a word usually have a long-vowel sound.

The following words are examples of this rule:

be **go** **hi** **my** **tutu**

(Sometimes the letter *y* can make a long-*e* sound at the end of a word, as in *daisy* and *funny*.)

Complete the following sentences with the single-vowel words from the box that follows.

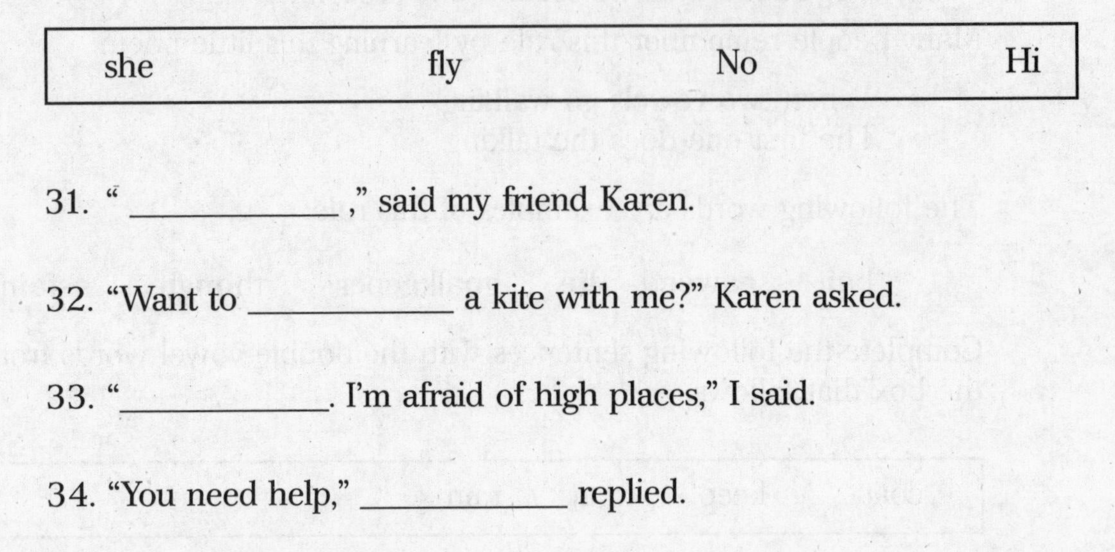

she	fly	No	Hi

31. "____________," said my friend Karen.

32. "Want to ____________ a kite with me?" Karen asked.

33. "____________. I'm afraid of high places," I said.

34. "You need help," ____________ replied.

TIP 10: Remember, there are some words that don't follow the rules. Some spelling patterns break the rules. Look at the following table of spelling patterns that don't follow the rules. Study the patterns and the sounds they make. Then, using the pictures as clues, write other examples of words that follow these spelling patterns.

Spelling Pattern	Sound	Examples	Your Example
-eigh	long-*a*	eight sleigh	____________
-ie	long-*e*	field niece	____________
-igh	long-*i*	right high	____________
-ow	long-*o*	grow flow	____________
-old -olt	long-*o*	told colt	____________
-ea	short-*e*	bread instead	____________

Sometimes, different spelling patterns have the same sound, such as the *ow* in *meow* and the *ou* in *loud.* And sometimes one spelling pattern can have two different sounds, such as the *oo* in *took* and *toot.*

Study the spelling patterns and sounds in the table that follows. Then write other examples of words that follow the patterns.

Spelling Pattern	Sound	Examples	Your Example(s)
-ow -ou	same sound	plow loud	__________ __________
-oo	two different sounds	cook boot	__________ __________
-oi -oy	same sound	boil joy	__________ __________

TIP 11: Different spelling patterns can make the same sound (rhyme).

As you can tell from the table on page 15, different spellings can make the same sound. Words that end with the same sound are called **rhymes**. Here are some examples of rhyming words that use different spelling patterns.

play / weigh   read / need   bite / night

Circle the correct answers to Numbers 35 through 37.

35. Which word rhymes with (makes the same sound as) the *aught* in *caught*?

A. bought
B. wrote
C. boast
D. boot

36. Which word rhymes with (makes the same sound as) the *ight* in *bright*?

A. sit
B. kite
C. hint
D. dirt

37. Which two words rhyme?

A. fire, fall
B. deal, peel
C. seal, male
D. peach, search

TIP 12: Remember word families.

There are many groups of words that share similar spellings. These are called **word families**. When you learn a new word, try to think of another word that is spelled almost the same way. This will help you sound out the new word. Look at the following word families.

the "ight" family

br**ight** r**ight**
l**ight** fl**ight**

the "oa" family

fl**oa**t f**oa**m
b**oa**t m**oa**n

the "ate" family

l**ate** st**ate**
g**ate** r**ate**

Other word families include *ite*, *ould*, *orn*, *ime*, and *ink*.

Circle the correct answers to Numbers 38 through 40.

38. Which word is in the same word family as *chain*?
   A. dart
   B. bald
   C. gain
   D. sale

39. Which word is in the same word family as *pink*?
   A. site
   B. link
   C. knee
   D. ripe

40. Which word is in the same word family as *time*?
   A. phase
   B. nine
   C. plunk
   D. crime

Word Sounds and Patterns
Lesson 1 Summary

When answering questions about word patterns, remember the following tips:

- Separate words into sounds or syllables.
- Some consonants can make either a hard sound or a soft sound.
- Consonants that stand together often combine their sounds.
- When a vowel is followed by an *r*, the *r* controls the vowel's sound.
- When a vowel is followed by one or more consonants (except *r*), it usually has a short-vowel sound.
- When a vowel is followed by a consonant and then a final *e*, it usually has a long-vowel sound. The *e* at the end is silent.
- When a vowel is followed by two consonants and a final *e*, it usually has a short-vowel sound. The final *e* is silent.
- Usually, when two vowels stand together, the first vowel has a long sound and the second one is silent.
- Single vowels (except *a*) at the end of a word usually have a long-vowel sound.
- Remember, there are some words that don't follow the rules.
- Different spelling patterns can make the same sound (rhyme).
- Remember word families.

CRCT Practice

Sample Word Pattern Questions

Directions: Circle the correct answer for each of the following questions.

Sam likes to <u>kick</u> the ball.

1. Which word begins with the same sound as *kick*?

A. kite

B. know

C. knock

D. cent

My favorite color is <u>blue</u>.

2. Which word begins with the same sound as *blue*?

A. base

B. brave

C. bush

D. black

My sister and I watched a boat race.

3. Which word has the same *a*-sound as the letter *a* in *race*?

A. far

B. bat

C. paper

D. ranch

I would also like a glass of milk.

4. Which word has the same *o*-sound as the letter *o* in *also*?

A. done

B. told

C. cost

D. shop

5. Which two words rhyme?

A. bite, sit

B. hair, smear

C. snack, grab

D. breeze, sneeze

6. Which two words rhyme?

A. through, blew

B. boil, call

C. shall, mall

D. close, closet

7. Which word is in the same word family as *late*?

A. rasp

B. gate

C. dart

D. path

Lesson 2

Understanding New Words

Overreacting / Over•re•*act*•ing
Nonburnable / Non•*burn*•able

Yikes! How can I ever learn to read words this long? Give me a break!

That's exactly what this lesson will give you–several breaks. You will learn how to break down a word into its separate parts.

Both of the long words at the start of this lesson are made up of **prefixes** (letters added to the beginning of a **root word**), the root word itself (set in *italic type* in the words above), and **suffixes** (letters added to the end of a root word).

Many words can be recognized and understood by looking at their prefixes, suffixes, and the main word, called the root word.

Let's work through an example:

> The root word *seal* means to *close tightly.* Adding the prefix *re-* changes the meaning to *seal again:* re*seal.* Adding the suffix *-able* changes the meaning to *able to be resealed:* re*seal*able.

Let's take a closer look at prefixes and what they mean.

TIP 1: A prefix is made by adding letters to the beginning of a root word.

A prefix is a set of letters added to the beginning of a root word. Adding a prefix changes the meaning of the root word.

Here's an example of a prefix at work:

un-	+	happy	=	unhappy
(prefix)		(root word)		(new word)

By adding *un-* to the root word *happy,* the meaning is changed. Now, instead of a good feeling (happy), we have the opposite: a bad feeling (unhappy).

There are many prefixes in the English language. Here are some prefixes you should know:

Prefix	**Meaning**	**Example** (***Prefix*** **+ Root Word = New Word)**
anti-	against	*anti* + freeze = antifreeze
bi-	two	*bi* + cycle = bicycle
co-	together, with	*co* + operate = cooperate
dis-	not, away from	*dis* + obey = disobey
fore-	in front	*fore* + head = forehead
im-	not	*im* + patient = impatient
in-	not	*in* + complete = incomplete
mid-	middle	*mid* + night = midnight
mis-	wrong, poorly	*mis* + spell = misspell
non-	not	*non* + sense = nonsense
over-	too much	*over* + due = overdue
pre-	before	*pre* + test = pretest
re-	again	*re* + paint = repaint
un-	not	*un* + fair = unfair

Practice Activity 1

Prefixes

Directions: Attach prefixes to the following words. The first one has been done for you.

1. *bi* + weekly = biweekly
2. *co* + pay = ____________
3. *dis* + continue = ____________
4. *im* + polite = ____________
5. *in* + direct = ____________
6. *mid* + day = ____________
7. *mis* + understand = ____________
8. *over* + run = ____________
9. *pre* + cook = ____________
10. *re* + do = ____________
11. *un* + able = ____________

Practice Activity 2

Prefixes

Directions: Read the following sentences. After each sentence, write a word that begins with a prefix and has the same meaning as the underlined words. The first one has been done for you. You may use the list of prefixes on page 24 to help you.

1. Paul lost the race. He wanted to <u>run it again</u>.

   rerun ______________________________

2. If you don't understand the story, <u>read it again</u>.

   ____

3. Shawna said that the story was <u>not true</u>.

   ____

4. Mother thought the babysitter was <u>paid too much</u>.

   ____

5. Tim's answer was <u>poorly understood</u>.

   ____

6. We will have lunch around <u>the middle of the day</u>.

   ____

7. This volcano is <u>not active</u>.

   ____

Practice Activity 3

Prefixes

Directions: Read the following sentences. Write the meaning of the underlined word on the line that follows each sentence. The first one has been done for you. You may use the prefix listing on page 24 to help you.

1. Justin's coach was displeased with his batting.

   not pleased

2. The airplane flew nonstop from Charleston to Chicago.

3. Roslyn's tickets had been prepaid.

4. I plan to rewrap this present before I give it to my teacher.

5. The old clock struck twelve times at midnight.

6. Carlos answered in an impolite way.

7. Amber and Cody often disagree about which television program to watch.

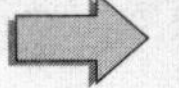

TIP 2: A suffix is made by adding letters to the end of a root word.

A suffix is a set of letters added to the end of a root word.

enjoy + *able* = enjoyable OR *able to be enjoyed*

When the suffix begins with a vowel, you must drop the silent *e*, as in the first example in the following list (love + *able* = lovable).

Suffix	Meaning	Example (Root Word + *Suffix* = New Word)
-able	able to be	love + *able* = lovable
-en	having the nature of, to make or become	gold + *en* = golden short + *en* = shorten
-er	one who does, that which	jump + *er* = jumper boil + *er* = boiler
-ence/-ance	state of being	differ + *ence* = difference import + *ance* = importance
-er	more	fast + *er* = faster
-est	most	fast + *est* = fastest
-ful	full of	beauty + *ful* = beautiful
-hood	state of	child + *hood* = childhood
-ion	in a state of	act + *ion* = action
-ish	being like	fool + *ish* = foolish
-ist	one who	art + *ist* = artist
-less	without	help + *less* = helpless
-ly	in such a way	sad + *ly* = sadly
-ment	in a state of	excite + *ment* = excitement
-ness	in a quality of or state of	silly + *ness* = silliness sick + *ness* = sickness
-ous	having a condition of or state of	danger + *ous* = dangerous

Practice Activity 4

Suffixes

Directions: Attach the suffix to each root word that follows. The first one has been done for you.

1. sad + *ness* = sadness ____________________
2. read + *able* = ____________________
3. fall + *en* = ____________________
4. teach + *er* = ____________________
5. help + *ful* = ____________________
6. loud + *est* = ____________________
7. thank + *ful* = ____________________
8. collect + *ion* = ____________________
9. enjoy + *ment* = ____________________
10. quick + *ly* = ____________________
11. joy + *ous* = ____________________

Practice Activity 5

Suffixes

Directions: Read the following sentences. After each sentence, write a word that ends with a suffix and has the same meaning as the underlined words. The first one has been done for you. You may use the list of suffixes on page 28 to help you.

1. These clothes are able to be washed.

   washable ______________________

2. Marco was full of hope for his team.

   ____

3. Javier's father is one who teaches.

   ____

4. Caitlin's desk is more neat than Martin's.

   ____

5. The fake money was without worth.

   ____

6. Ramone always showed a quality or state of being good.

   ____

7. The young deer moved in a silent way.

   ____

8. This tomato is the most large.

____

9. Receiving the award made Gerri full of thanks.

____

10. The crowd was in a state of joy.

____

Practice Activity 6

Suffixes

Directions: Read the following sentences. Write the meaning of the underlined word on the line that follows each sentence. The first one has been done for you. You may use the suffix listing on page 28 to help you.

1. My kitten, Muffin, is very lovable.

   able to be loved

2. Marta used bleach to whiten her socks.

   ____

3. With a score of 113 to 6, winning the game seemed hopeless.

   ____

4. The little mouse moved quietly.

   ____

5. Jaime's bike is faster than mine.

____

6. Mrs. Maldonado is my teacher.

____

7. Karen's grandmother is filled with kindness.

____

8. Jamal held the bat tightly.

____

9. Fernando is always helpful to others.

____

10. The Nile is the longest river in the world.

____

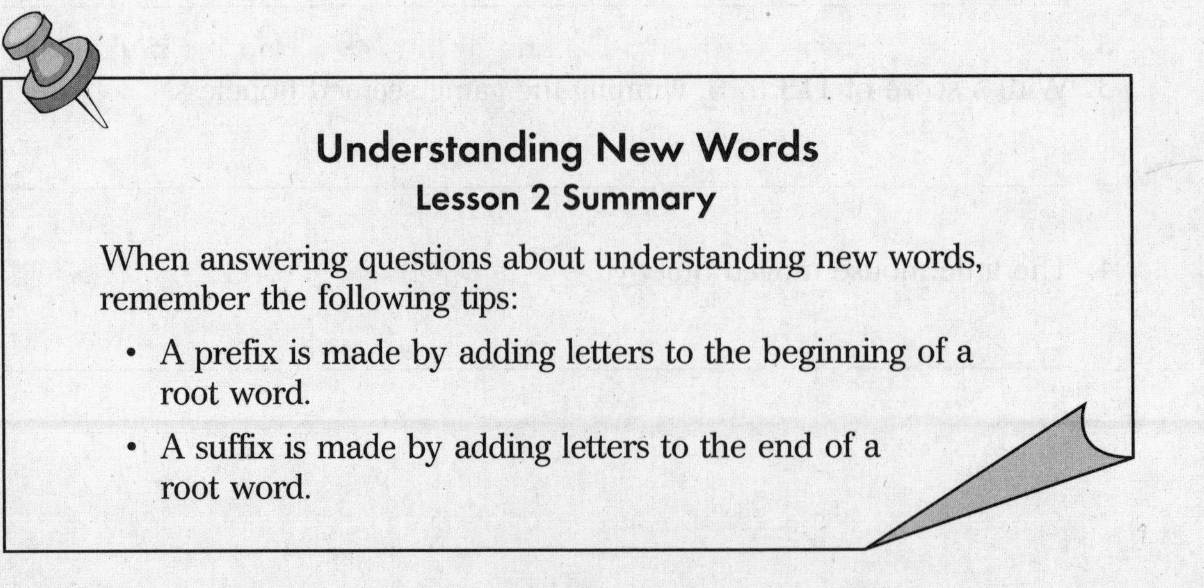

Understanding New Words
Lesson 2 Summary

When answering questions about understanding new words, remember the following tips:

- A prefix is made by adding letters to the beginning of a root word.
- A suffix is made by adding letters to the end of a root word.

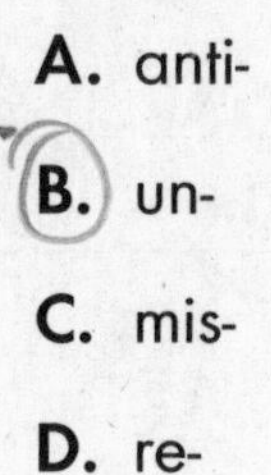

CRCT Practice

Sample New Words Questions

Directions: Circle the correct answer for each of the following questions.

1. **Which prefix can you add to *sure* to make it mean *not sure*?**

   A. anti-

   B. un-

   C. mis-

   D. re-

2. **Which prefix can you add to *author* to make it mean *author together*?**

   A. co-

   B. bi-

   C. mid-

   D. fore-

3. **Which suffix can you add to the end of the word *clean* to make it mean *more clean*?**

   A. -ly

   B. -er

   C. -able

   D. -est

4. Which suffix can you add to the end of the word *laugh* to make it mean *able to laugh*?

A. -en

B. -ful

C. -ness

D. -able

5. What is the root of *comfortable*?

A. come

B. fort

C. comfort

D. able

6. What is the root of *peaceful*?

A. pea

B. ace

C. ful

D. peace

Lesson 3

Word Power

Did you know there are about a million words in the English language? This means that all of us—third graders, teachers, store workers, authors, and many other people—sometimes see words we don't know.

Whether you are reading a comic book or a social studies book, there is a chance that you will *confront* (meet) a word that is *alien* (strange) to you. Don't *fret* (worry)!

When you see a new word that makes no sense to you, don't give up. Be a detective, just like Sherlock Holmes. Look for clues to help you figure out the word.

As you read the story about Sherlock Holmes, think about how you might figure out what the unknown words mean.

Sherlock Holmes and the Case of the Wheediddle

by Sandi Shaw

Sherlock Holmes put his violin back in its case. He stared once again at the note that had been slipped under his door. It was very, very strange. The writer had used many words that Sherlock and his partner, Dr. Watson, did not know. Holmes would have to look for clues to understand the note.

Daab Mr. Holmes,

Can we meet at 8 o'grock? Wait for me. I hope I'm not lorgh. Sometimes I forget to wind my wheediddle and it stops. Then I don't know what time it is. I'll meet you at the bongle of Baker Street and 10th Avenue. Try not to be lorgh!

Very truly yongs,
Hobart Tinwhistle

"Well," said Sherlock, "**Daab** must mean *Dear* since most letters begin with that word.

"And **o'grock** could mean *o'clock,* since it is matched with the number 8."

The great detective continued to study the letter. "**Wheediddle** must mean *watch* or *clock,* since the writer says that his wheediddle stops when he doesn't wind it–and then he doesn't know what time it is.

"**Lorgh** must mean *late.* He hopes he won't be late if his watch stops. Then, later in the note, he tells me not to be **lorgh.** Yes, I am certain that **lorgh** means *late,*" Sherlock said to himself. "**Bongle** must mean *corner,* since Baker Street crosses 10th Avenue.

"And, finally," the detective said, "**yongs** must mean *yours.* Mr. Tinwhistle is probably trying to close his letter with 'Very truly yours.'

"Dr. Watson!" Sherlock called excitedly. "Come. Grab your coat and hat. We must meet a certain Mr. Tinwhistle at the corner of Baker Street and 10th Avenue at 8 o'clock. And," he added, "we must not be 'lorgh'!"

TIP 1: Don't stop reading when you come to a word you don't know.

The best way to understand a new word is to use other words you already know to help you. So don't stop reading just because you don't know a word. Say it to yourself, then go right on reading.

Sometimes, other words in the passage will give clues to the meaning of the new word. These words often are found close together–or even in the same sentence. Look at these examples:

1) In this area, we can find gabbro, a type of dark, heavy rock.
2) She looked in her coin purse and found one dinar.
3) Tom assured his friend that he would help him build a treehouse.

1. What is *gabbro?*

____

2. What is a *dinar?*

____

3. What is the meaning of *assured?*

____

4. Look back at Mr. Tinwhistle's letter on page 35. Underline details that give clues to the meaning of *wheedidle.*

TIP 2: Go back to the passage and put your finger on the unknown word.

When a question on a reading test asks you about the meaning of a word or a *phrase* (group of words), first go back to the passage and find the word or phrase. Don't just try to guess its meaning without looking back at the passage to see how it is used.

Once you find the word, put your finger on it. This will help you keep your place.

TIP 3: Read the sentences around the unknown word.

If you still don't understand the word, read the whole paragraph. While reading, look carefully for clues that will help you figure out the meaning. Once you've found all the clues you can, make your best guess.

Read the following paragraph. It tells about an imaginary thing called a *grundle.* Try to figure out what a *grundle* is.

> **Grundles** are beautiful and very useful. A full-grown grundle is big enough to make shade in the summer. In the spring, its blossoms have a wonderful smell. A grundle has strong branches that hold a lot of juicy fruit.

5. What do you know about a *grundle* from reading the paragraph?

____

____

6. In this paragraph, a *grundle* is a
   A. tree.
   B. weed.
   C. flower.
   D. vegetable.

TIP 4: Try each multiple-choice answer in place of the unknown word.

Plugging in the multiple-choice answers one at a time may help you to find the right answer.

When you are asked the meaning of a word, find the sentence in the passage. Replace the unknown word with each answer choice, one at a time. The answer that makes the most sense is probably correct.

Read the following paragraph.

> I think most people called her Peggy the Pumpkin Princess. Remember, now, that was a long time ago. To the best of my recollection, she never called herself by that name. In fact, she hated pumpkins–and her real name was Agnes.

Read the following question, but don't answer it yet.

7. Which word means the same as *recollection*?
   A. eyesight
   B. memory
   C. touch
   D. smell

First, find the sentence that contains the underlined word *recollection.* Then, try each answer choice in place of the word *recollection.* Which answer choice makes the most sense in the sentence?

Now go back and answer the question.

TIP 5: Check the passage for words with the same meaning (synonyms).

If you read a word that you don't know, you will probably find all sorts of clues to the word's meaning in the story or passage.

Sometimes, the story will have other words with nearly the same meaning as the word you are trying to figure out. Words with nearly the same meaning are called **synonyms.**

Read the following paragraph, then answer Numbers 8 and 9.

> The old man was very poor. Each day he would **labor** in his field until he was so tired that he could barely move. As the sun set, the old man would stop his hard work. Then he would throw his hoe over his shoulder and slowly walk home to his small cottage.

8. Underline any words or phrases in the paragraph that you think might be close to the same meaning as the word *labor.*

9. Which word is a synonym for the word *labor*?
   A. work
   B. laugh
   C. wander
   D. daydream

TIP 6: Check the passage for words with opposite meanings (antonyms).

Sometimes the passage will give you clues to the opposite meanings of a word. A word that means the opposite of another word is called an **antonym.** If you can figure out a word's opposite, you can make a good guess about its meaning. Read the following sentence, then answer questions 10 and 11.

Although Carmen was usually very **prompt** for her music lesson, today she was 10 minutes late.

10. Underline any words in the sentence that you think might have the opposite meaning of *prompt.*

11. Which word is an antonym for the word *prompt?*
    A. sad
    B. late
    C. puzzled
    D. unhappy

TIP 7: Watch out for words that are spelled the same and pronounced the same but have different meanings (multiple-meaning words).

Words that are spelled the same and pronounced the same but have different meanings are called **multiple-meaning words.**

Read each of the following sentences. Then, write a sentence of your own using the word in **boldface** with a different meaning. The first one has been done for you.

12. From our fishing boat, we could see a **school** of fish.

    The children rode the bus to school.
    ____

13. The class **rose** to its feet.

    ____

    ____

14. The bird has a yellow **bill.**

____

____

15. Queen Elizabeth II is Britain's **ruler.**

____

____

TIP 8: Check the passage for words that are pronounced the same but have different spellings and meanings (homophones).

Words that are pronounced the same but have different spellings and meanings are called **homophones.** Some of the most common homophones are the words *to* (as in *to go*), *too* (as in *also*), and *two* (as in *one plus one*).

Read each of the following sentences. Then write a word of your own that is pronounced the same as the word in *italic type* but is spelled differently.

16. Bob *ate* his dinner. ____________________

17. The wind *blew.* ____________________

18. John wants to *buy* a hamburger. ____________________

TIP 9: Check the passage for words that are spelled the same but are pronounced differently and have different meanings (homographs).

Words that are spelled the same but are pronounced differently and have different meanings are called **homographs.** An example of a homograph is the word *bow.* It can mean a *bow* (rhymes with *low*) on a birthday present or a *bow* that shoots arrows. It can also mean to *bow* (rhymes with *cow*) from the waist or the *bow* of a ship.

Read each of the following sentences. Complete the second sentence using the word in *italic type* so that it is pronounced differently and has a different meaning.

Keiko broke the *lead* in her pencil.

19. Our guide will ____________ the way.

Carlo has a *live* rabbit for a pet.

20. Where does Amber ____________ ?

Don't forget to *wind* the old alarm clock.

21. There is a strong north ____________ blowing today.

TIP 10: Watch out for special word uses.

Many writers and speakers use **idioms.** An idiom, sometimes called a **figure of speech**, is a special way of saying one thing but meaning another. If your teacher tells you to "hold your tongue," she or he doesn't really mean you should grab your tongue with your hand. Your teacher is just saying, "Please be quiet."

Here are some idioms, or figures of speech. Write the meanings of those you know on the line that follows each idiom. The first one is done for you.

22. Give me a hand.

    Help me out.

23. I'm walking on air.

    ____

24. Don't put your foot in your mouth.

    ____

25. You're pulling my leg.

    ____

26. The joke cracked me up.

    ____

27. It broke my heart.

    ____

28. On the lines that follow, write another idiom you know.

____

____

____

____

Word Power

Lesson 3 Summary

When answering questions about word power, remember the following tips:

- Don't stop reading when you come to a word you don't know.
- Go back to the passage and put your finger on the unknown word.
- Read the sentences around the unknown word.
- Try each multiple-choice answer in place of the unknown word.
- Check the passage for words with the same meaning (synonyms).
- Check the passage for words with opposite meanings (antonyms).
- Watch out for words that are spelled the same and pronounced the same but have different meanings (multiple-meaning words).
- Check the passage for words that are pronounced the same but have different spellings and meanings (homophones).
- Check the passage for words that are spelled the same but are pronounced differently and have different meanings (homographs).
- Watch out for special word uses.

CRCT Practice

Directions: Read the passage, then answer the questions.

The First Brothers of Flight

by Ted Remington

About 100 years before the Wright brothers were born, Jacques (*Zhock*) and Joseph Montgolfier (*Mahn-GAHL-fee-ay*) lived in a little town not far from Paris, France. One day, Joseph threw a paper bag into a fire. Before it could burn, the bag floated up the chimney. This gave the men an idea.

The hot air captured inside the bag must be lighter than the cool air around it, they thought. That would make the bag rise. To test their idea, they made a balloon and filled it with hot air. It rose off the ground as the paper bag had. Their idea had been right!

The brothers made larger and larger balloons. They wanted to make a balloon big enough to carry a person into the sky. If their plan worked, Jacques and Joseph's balloon would be the world's first flying machine.

The brothers finally made a balloon big enough to carry two people. But what if their balloon fell? The passengers could be hurt–or worse. They decided to send up animals instead of people. The very first hot air balloon passengers were a goat, a duck, and a rooster. After a smooth and gentle flight, the animals landed softly in a treetop two miles away. The brothers decided it was time to send a person aloft.

On November 21, 1783, a great crowd watched the men fill their giant balloon. At the sound of a cannon, the brothers untied the ropes that held the balloon to the ground. Two daring young Frenchmen (not the Montgolfier brothers) began to lift slowly into the air.

Finally, the blue and gold balloon rose high into the sky. It glided silently and calmly over the rooftops of Paris, far above the cheering people. After floating five miles, the brave passengers landed gently on the ground. The trip had lasted 20 minutes.

Thanks to Jacques and Joseph Montgolfier, a whole new way of traveling became possible. The world would never be the same.

Sample Word Power Questions

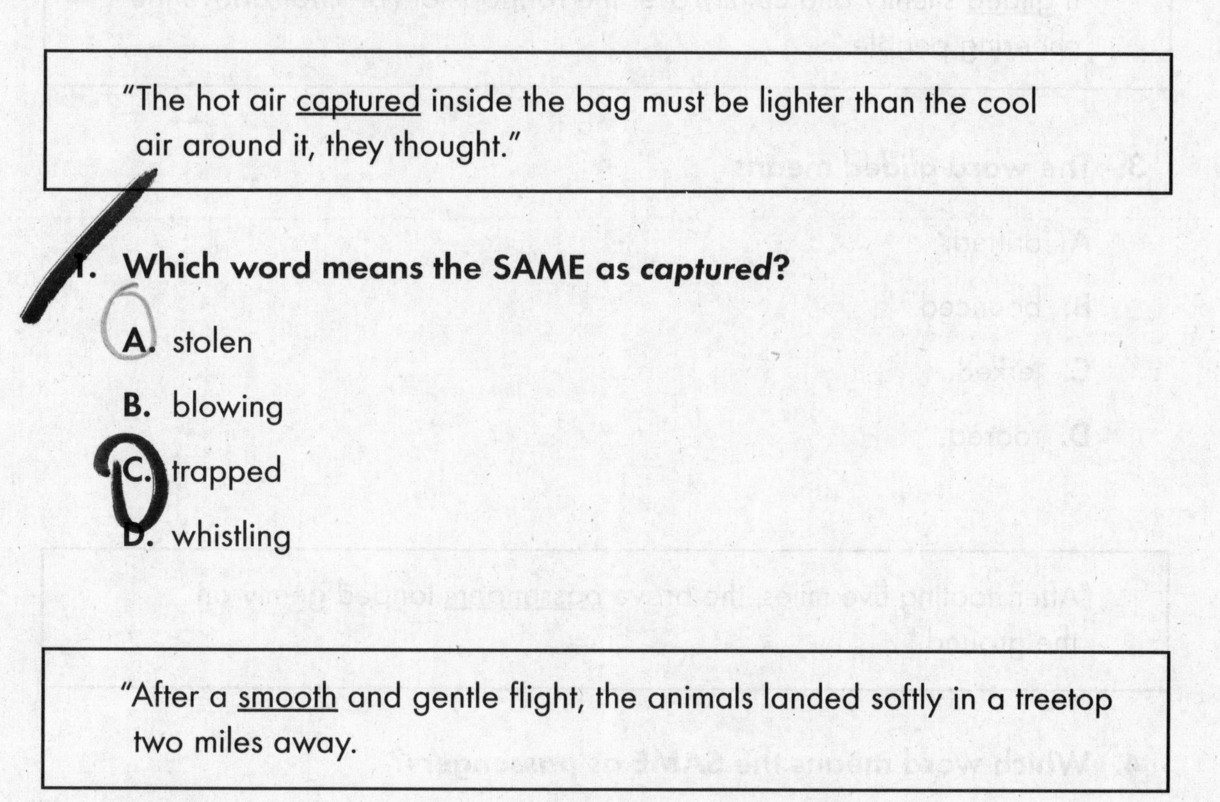

"The hot air captured inside the bag must be lighter than the cool air around it, they thought."

1. Which word means the SAME as *captured*?

A. stolen

B. blowing

C. trapped

D. whistling

"After a smooth and gentle flight, the animals landed softly in a treetop two miles away.

2. Which word means the OPPOSITE of *smooth*?

A. rough

B. long

C. quiet

D. high

> "It glided silently and calmly over the rooftops of Paris, far above the cheering people."

3. The word *glided* means

A. drifted.

B. bounced.

C. jerked.

D. roared.

> "After floating five miles, the brave passengers landed gently on the ground."

4. Which word means the SAME as *passengers*?

A. goats

B. riders

C. animals

D. brothers

Additional Practice Questions

5. Which prefix can you add to *wash* to make it mean *wash again*?

A. bi-

B. re-

C. mis-

D. post-

6. Which suffix can you add to the end of the word *child* to make it mean *being like a child*?

A. -est

B. -ish

C. -ness

D. -ist

7. Which two words rhyme?

A. pond, wrong

B. half, high

C. real, sleigh

D. great, state

8. What is the root word of *thinking*?

A. thin

B. ink

C. king

D. think

Lesson 4

Finding New Words

A supermarket has all kinds of food, plus toothpaste, medicine, laundry soap, hand soap, dish soap (lots of soap!), and many other things your family needs.

Each area is set up with a certain kind of food or product so you can find things more easily. Do you need bread? Go to the bread aisle. Do you need milk? There's the dairy case.

Even though you don't need a grocery cart, finding information in a library is a lot like going to a supermarket. Everything you need is there. You just need to know where to find it.

First of all, this lesson will review how to sound out unknown words. This is a necessary skill for using many reference books. Then you will get a chance to practice with such things as a **dictionary** and a **thesaurus**.

In fact, this lesson will show you how to go shopping for all kinds of information. Unlike buying things in a supermarket, this shopping trip will cost you nothing.

TIP 1: A dictionary will help you learn new words.

Imagine you are busily reading when you come upon a word you don't know. If nothing else in the passage helps you, then it's time to go shopping for information. The best place to look for a new word is in a dictionary.

Look at this example of a dictionary page:

kilowatt | knapsack 323

a	hat	**i**	it	**oi**	oil	**ch**	child	**ə =**	**a** in about
ā	age	**ī**	ice	**ou**	out	**ng**	long		**e** in taken
ä	far	**o**	hot	**u**	cup	**sh**	she		**i** in pencil
e	let	**ō**	open	**u̇**	put	**th**	thin		**o** in lemon
ē	equal	**ô**	order	**ü**	rule	**ŦH**	then		**u** in circus
ėr	term					**zh**	measure		

kil o watt (kil′ə wot′), a unit for measuring electric power equal to 1000 watts. *noun.*

kilt (kilt), a pleated skirt, reaching to the knees, worn by men in parts of Scotland. *noun.*

ki mo no (kə mō′nə), **1** a loose outer garment held in place by a sash, worn by both men and women in Japan. **2** a woman's loose dressing gown. *noun, plural* **ki mo nos.**

kin (kin), **1** family or relatives; kindred: *All our kin came to the family reunion.* **2** family relationship: *What kin is she to you?* **3** related: *Your cousin is also kin to me.* 1, 2 *noun,* 3 *adjective.*
next of kin, nearest living relative.

kind[1] (kīnd), **1** friendly; doing good rather than harm: *A kind person tries to help others. Sharing your lunch was a kind thing to do.* **2** gentle: *Be kind to animals. adjective.*

kind[2] (kīnd), **1** sort; type: *I like many kinds of food. A kilt is a kind of skirt.* **2** natural group: *The wolf hunted in a pack with others of its kind. noun.*
of a kind, of the same sort: *The cakes were all of a kind—chocolate.*

from *Scott, Foresman Beginning Dictionary*

Practice Activity 1

Dictionary

Directions: Use the dictionary page to answer the following questions.

1. Who would most likely wear a *kimono?*
   A. someone from Japan
   B. someone from Scotland
   C. someone who fixes cars
   D. someone who exercises at the gym

2. The letter *i* in *kind* is pronounced the same as the *i* in
   A. it.
   B. ice.
   C. thin.
   D. pencil.

3. The word *kin* can be used as
   A. a noun and a verb.
   B. an adjective and a verb.
   C. an adjective and a noun.
   D. an adjective and an adverb.

Word Hunt

New words are like gifts we can use again and again. For fun, use a dictionary to find a new word that you can make your own. Think of it as an adventure. Open up the dictionary to any page. Look at the words and their meanings. Be sure you are saying the word as it is supposed to be said. Then, when you have your new word, you can share it with the rest of the class.

TIP 2: Use a thesaurus to find words with the same or nearly the same meaning.

Like a dictionary, a **thesaurus** is a list of words in alphabetical order. But instead of telling you what each word means, a thesaurus gives several other words that mean the same or nearly the same thing. You learned in Lesson 3 that these words are called **synonyms.**

You might be writing a report about the hottest place in the United States–Death Valley, California. You might want to use other words that mean the same as *hot.* If you looked up hot in a thesaurus, you would find words such as *baking, blistering, boiling, burning, fiery, heated, scalding, scorching,* and *sizzling.*

Here's how a thesaurus page might look:

Thesaurus Sample

beach[1] (*noun*)	shore, shoreline, seashore, seaside, seafront, waterfront
beach[2] (*verb*)	run aground, run on the rocks, run onto land
below (*prep.*)	under, beneath, underneath
build[1] (*verb*)	create, make, erect, set up, get up, put together, piece together
build[2] (*noun*)	form, shape, figure, frame

Most thesaurus entries have similar information. The entry for beach[1] tells you a lot. The word (noun) following beach[1] means that the word is a noun. The word (verb) following beach[2] means that the second word beach is a verb. (Abbreviations for parts of speech are sometimes used. Some of those abbreviations include n. for noun, v. for verb, prep. for preposition, and adj. for adjective.)

Because synonyms mean almost the same thing, not every synonym listed will have the exact meaning you want for your sentence. Be sure you pick the one with the right meaning.

Practice Activity 2

Thesaurus

Directions: Use the sample thesaurus on page 53 to answer the following questions.

1. What kind of word is *below?*
   A. verb
   B. noun
   C. adjective
   D. preposition

2. Which of these words means the same as the word *beach*[2]?
   A. shoreline
   B. seafront
   C. run aground
   D. waterfront

Directions: Use a thesaurus to find three words that have the same meaning as the word *cold.* Write them on the lines below.

3. ______________________________

4. ______________________________

5. ______________________________

Directions: Use a thesaurus to find three words that have the same meaning as the word *shake.* Write them on the lines below.

6. ______________________________

7. ______________________________

8. ______________________________

TIP 3: Use a glossary to better understand the meanings of words.

Some books have a **glossary**, which is like a dictionary of important words in the book. The glossary lists words in alphabetical order. It is found near the back of a book. Here is part of a glossary from a third-grade science book.

accurate	as exact as possible (page 6)
balanced diet	a diet that gives your body everything it needs to stay healthy and to grow (page 17)
basic needs	things that all living creatures must have in order to live: food, water, clean air, and shelter (page 15)
biologist	a scientist who studies living things (page 14)
category	a grouping of similar things (pages 2, 6)
characteristic	a part, feature, or action of an animal, plant, or thing that can be used to compare it with other animals, plants, or things (pages 3, 4, 21)
chemical change	when one kind of matter changes into a different kind of matter (page 10)
claim	a statement someone wants us to believe is true (page 33)

Practice Activity 3

Glossary

Directions: Use the sample glossary on page 55 to help you answer the following questions.

1. On which page could you read about "basic needs"?
   A. 6
   B. 15
   C. 21
   D. 28

2. Which of the following BEST describes the word *accurate*?
   A. exact
   B. healthy
   C. scientist
   D. special

Finding New Words
Lesson 4 Summary

When answering questions about word power, remember the following tips:

- A dictionary will help you learn new words.
- Use a thesaurus to find words with the same or nearly the same meaning.
- Use a glossary to better understand the meanings of words.

CRCT Practice

Sample Finding New Words Questions

Directions: Use the following definition from a dictionary to answer Numbers 1 through 3.

herd (herd), **1** a group of animals that move and feed together: *The buffalo herd moved into the valley.* **2** a large group of people. **3** come together: *They herded together to get warm.* **4** move a group of people or animals; drive: *The farmer herded his cows toward the barn.* **1, 2** *noun;* **3, 4** *verb.*

"The cowboys are moving a large herd of cattle down the trail."

1. What is the meaning of *herd* as it is used in this sentence?

A. meaning 1

B. meaning 2

C. meaning 3

D. meaning 4

2. The word *herd* can be used as

A. a noun and a verb.

B. only a noun.

C. only a verb.

D. an adjective.

3. Which meaning of *herd* means to *come together*?

A. meaning 1

B. meaning 2

C. meaning 3

D. meaning 4

Directions: Use the following entry from a thesaurus to answer Numbers 4 and 5.

Thesaurus Sample

warm[1] *adj.*	lukewarm, slightly heated; caring; showing feeling.
warm[2] *v.*	to heat; bake.

4. Which of these words means nearly the same as the word *warm*[2]?

A. hot

B. cook

C. love

D. friendly

5. What kind of word is *bake*?

A. noun

B. verb

C. adjective

D. adverb

Directions: Use the following glossary from a book about rain forests to answer Numbers 6 and 7.

mammals	warm-blooded animals (page 7)
mandrill	large, brightly colored monkey (page 3, 24)
manus	term for the hand of an animal (page 34)
margay	a wild cat that is mostly active at night (page 2, 42)
marsupial	mammal with a pouch to carry its young (page 10, 29, 31)
migration	movement of a large group of animals (page 8, 22, 24, 32)
molt	the shedding of an animal's skin or feathers (page 15)

6. On which page could you read about "mammals"?

A. page 3

B. page 7

C. page 10

D. page 15

7. Which of the following BEST describes *migration*?

A. monkey

B. movement

C. mammal

D. molt

Additional Practice Questions

Marsha asked her grandmother to <u>mend</u> her torn jacket.

8. Which word means the same as *mend*?

A. fix

B. find

C. buy

D. wear

9. What suffix can you add to the end of the word *play* to make it mean *full of play*?

A. -ish

B. -ful

C. -hood

D. -able

Rami finished the difficult race, running an entire mile without stopping to rest.

10. Which word means the OPPOSITE of *difficult*?

A. long

B. easy

C. fast

D. tough

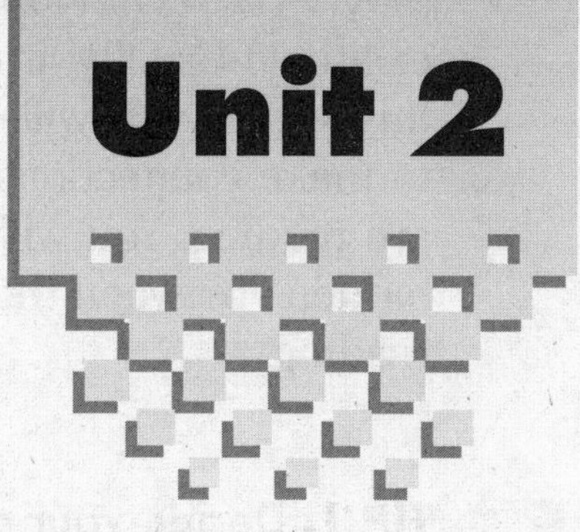

Understanding What You Read

When you read a book, are you more interested in the "big picture," or do you look for the little details? As you will see in this unit, both are necessary. This unit will help you spot important details. It will also show you how those details work together to support the main idea.

You will learn that authors sometimes compare one thing to another. You will find that authors tell their readers what causes certain things to happen in their stories. And, you will learn how to think about what you have read and to decide what it means.

In This Unit

Lesson 5

Hints for Better Reading

Writers can be tricky. They don't always tell you everything when they write. (They do this to make their stories more interesting and exciting.) Usually, it is up to you to figure things out for yourself. In this lesson, you will learn some tips to do just that. You will learn how to make connections between what you already know and what you are reading. You will also learn how to figure out what the author has hidden "between the lines." As you will see, that's part of the fun of reading.

TIP 1: Decide your purpose for reading.

You will have a much easier time getting the right information from a story or passage if you know why you are reading it. Are you reading for enjoyment, trying to solve a problem, following directions, trying to make a decision about something, or taking a reading test? For example, if you and your family wanted to visit President Franklin Roosevelt's Little White House at Warm Springs, you might visit a library for the purpose of learning about the history of the Little White House.

TIP 2: Take time to preview a passage or a book before you read it.

Here are some things you can do to preview books or passages.

- To help you get a "feel" for what you are about to read, **preview** the book or passage. When you preview a passage or book, you look it over before you begin reading.
- Read the title. In a book, also look for **chapter headings** (chapter names). Check for headlines that break a passage or a book chapter into parts (like the tips in this book).
- Look at the **table of contents**. The table of contents is an outline of a book. It gives you a list of chapter headings and the page number where that chapter can be found. The table of contents is usually found in the first few pages of a book.

Here is a table of contents from a book about dogs.

Table of Contents

Circle the correct answer for Numbers 1 and 2.

1. Which page would you turn to if you wanted to know what kind of food to give your dog?
   A. 21
   B. 32
   C. 41
   D. 57

2. Which page would you turn to if you wanted to teach your dog to fetch a ball?
   A. 32
   B. 41
   C. 57
   D. 71

More things to preview

- Look at any pictures or drawings that go with the passage or book. Read the captions (writing that goes with a picture or photograph). An example of a caption can be found on page 90 of this book.
- Check for special kinds of type, like **bold**, underlined, *italic,* or ALL CAPITAL letters. Words in special type are usually very important.
- Read the introduction to the book or passage, if there is one.
- Then begin your careful reading of the book or passage.

TIP 3: Link your reading to your life experiences.

Later in this lesson, you will read a passage about the game *Rock, Paper, Scissors.* But before you do, think about what you already know about the topic. Do you know a version of this game already? Have you seen others playing it? Keep asking yourself these kinds of questions before you read a passage.

Also, ask yourself what you wish to learn about a topic. A helpful way to do this is by using a K-W-L chart. "K" stands for what you ***know,*** "W" stands for what you ***want to know,*** and "L" stands for what you ***learned*** about the topic while reading the passage.

3. What do you know about the game *Rock, Paper, Scissors?* Write anything that comes to mind in the "K" part of the chart. In the "W" part of the chart, write down some questions you might have about the topic. For now, leave the "L" part of the chart empty. You will come back to that later.

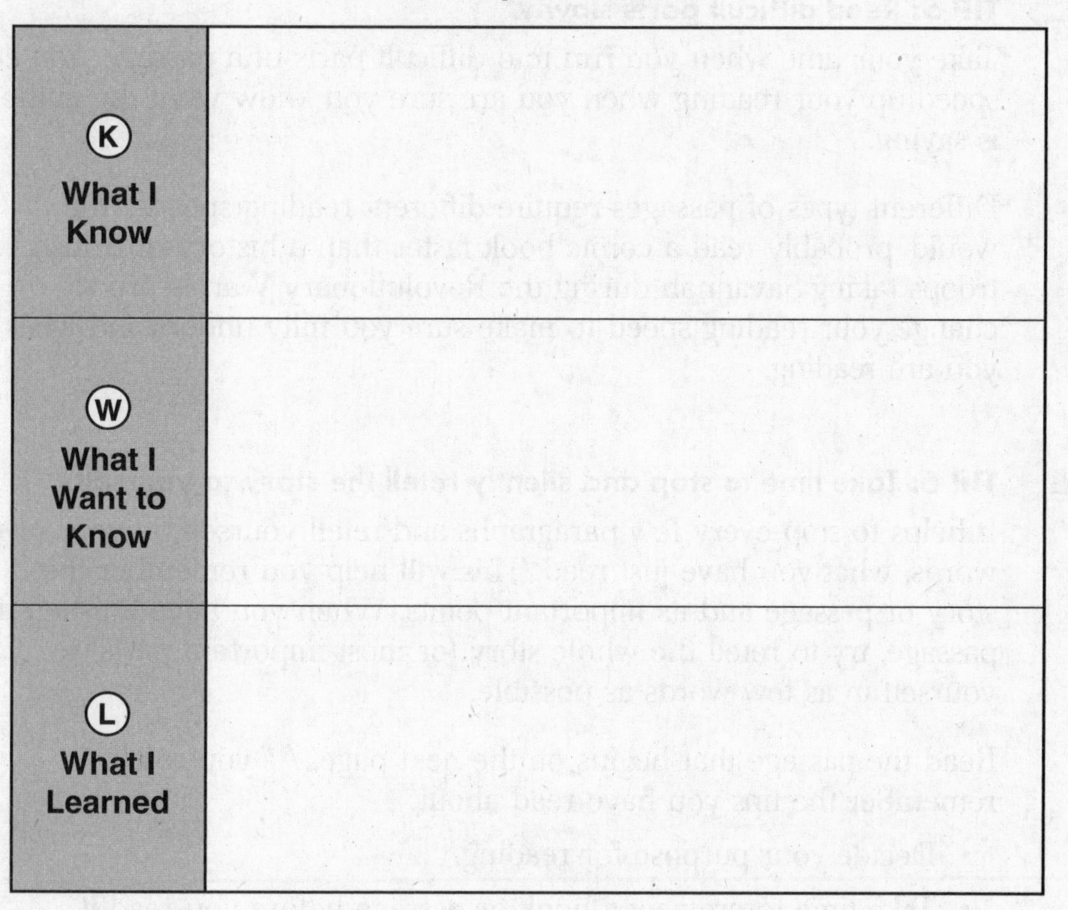

TIP 4: Ask questions as you read.

As you begin reading, ask yourself questions such as the following:

- Do I understand what the author is saying?
- Does this make sense to me?
- What is this passage mostly about?
- How does all this information add up?

Mark any parts of the passage that seem difficult to understand. You may wish to go back to those parts later.

TIP 5: Read difficult parts slowly.

Take your time when you run into difficult parts of a passage. You can speed up your reading when you are sure you know what the author is saying.

Different types of passages require different reading speeds. You would probably read a comic book faster than a history of British troops taking Savannah during the Revolutionary War. Learn to change your reading speed to make sure you fully understand what you are reading.

TIP 6: Take time to stop and silently retell the story to yourself.

It helps to stop every few paragraphs and retell yourself, in your own words, what you have just read. This will help you remember the story or passage and its important points. When you have finished the passage, try to retell the whole story (or most important parts) to yourself in as few words as possible.

Read the passage that begins on the next page. As you read, remember the tips you have read about.

- Decide your purpose for reading.
- Take time to preview a book or passage before you read it.
- Link your reading to your life experiences.
- Ask questions as you read.
- Read difficult parts slowly.
- Take time to stop and silently retell the story to yourself.

Ching! Chang! Pok!

by Christine Thomas

As you read this passage, you may find that you have more ideas or questions to write in your K-W-L chart. Continue to make connections between the passage and what you have learned in your life, and jot those connections down in your chart.

Imagine that you are walking down a street in Beijing, China. You come upon a group of boys and girls playing a game. Two of the boys each wave a fist up and down and chant, *"Ching! Chang! Pok!"* Even though you have never heard these words before, you probably know who wins the game. One boy shows two fingers, and the other shows a flat hand. You know the first boy wins because scissors beat paper in *Rock, Paper, Scissors.*

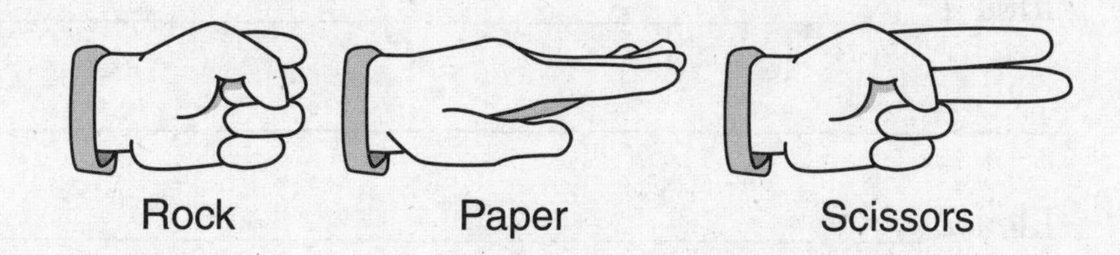

You have probably seen or played *Rock, Paper, Scissors* many times, but you might not know that the game began many years ago in Asia and is now played in almost every country in the world. Since its beginnings, the game has taken many different forms, but certain parts of the game are always the same. In most forms of the game, two or three players raise their fists, bouncing them up and down as they chant the words for each sign of the game. For example, in Japan, the players shout, *"Ishi! Hasami! Kami!"* (rock, scissors, paper). The third time they raise their fists, each player makes a sign for rock (a fist), scissors (two fingers), or paper (a flat hand). In the game, rock breaks scissors, scissors cut paper, and paper covers rock. The person showing the strongest sign wins.

So the next time you need to make an important decision—like who gets to be first in line, or who gets to have the last piece of pizza—don't flip a coin. Play a quick game of *Ching! Chang! Pok!*

TIP 7: After you retell the story or passage to yourself, decide what it is mostly about.

Take a minute to think about the main idea of the story or passage. Then, if you need to, go back and skim the passage for the most important points that support the main idea.

4. This story is MAINLY about how children around the world

   A. play the same game.
   B. use two fingers for a scissors.
   C. say, "Ching! Chang! Pok!"
   D. wave their fists up and down.

5. List at least two ideas that support the main idea of *"Ching! Chang! Pok!"*

   Idea 1 ________________________________

   ____

   Idea 2 ________________________________

   ____

"Ching! Chang! Pok!" is an example of nonfiction (writing that gives information about real things). If you are reading a made-up story, retell the most important events in your mind. Ask yourself questions such as, *How did the main characters solve their problem?* You will learn more about made-up stories in Lesson 9.

TIP 8: Learn to "read between the lines."

Have you ever heard the saying "read between the lines"? It just means figuring out what all the information adds up to. What is the author's main message? Authors usually don't tell you every single thing in plain language. Instead, they make their writing more interesting by leaving some things for you to figure out.

6. In English, *ching, chang, pok* means
   A. *win, lose, tie.*
   B. *fist, fingers, hand.*
   C. *rock, paper, scissors.*
   D. *ready, set, go.*

See how easy it is to read between the lines? In *"Ching! Chang! Pok!,"* the author doesn't come right out and say that *"Ching! Chang! Pok!"* is the same thing as *"Rock, Paper, Scissors."* Instead, she says that if you saw people playing the game *Ching! Chang! Pok!* in China, you would be able to understand what they're playing by the actions they make with their hands.

TIP 9: Study charts, pictures, and drawings again during your careful reading of the passage.

Whenever the author includes things to look at–such as pictures or drawings–they're probably there for a reason. Ask yourself: *Does the drawing tell me something important? Does this picture say something that is not included in the passage?* Think about why the author chose to include them.

7. How does the drawing of the hands help you better understand the game of *Rock, Paper, Scissors*?

____

____

____

TIP 10: Write down what you learned from the passage in your K-W-L chart.

This is the best part of making a K-W-L chart. Now that you have learned some new information about the game *Rock, Paper, Scissors,* go back and fill in the "L" part of your chart. Try to list as many new facts as you can, based on the passage.

8. How does the K-W-L chart help you to understand the passage?

____

____

____

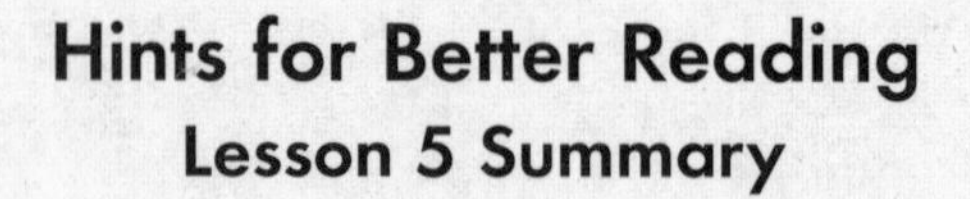

Hints for Better Reading

Lesson 5 Summary

When reading any story or passage, remember the following tips:

- Decide your purpose for reading.
- Take time to preview a book or passage before you read it.
- Link your reading to your life experiences.
- Ask questions as you read.
- Read difficult parts slowly.
- Take time to stop and silently retell the story to yourself.
- After you retell the story or passage to yourself, decide what it is mostly about.
- Learn to "read between the lines."
- Study charts, pictures, and drawings again during your careful reading of the passage.
- Write down what you learned from the passage in your K-W-L chart.

CRCT Practice

Directions: Read the passage, and then answer the questions.

The Biggest Animal That Ever Lived

by A. J. Gardner

What are the biggest animals that ever lived? Are they elephants? Elephants are pretty big compared to people, but they're not the biggest animals ever. Could they be giant dinosaurs like the tyrannosaur (tuh-RAN-uh-SAWR)? When those animals lived, millions of years ago, they were bigger than elephants are today. But dinosaurs weren't the biggest animals, either.

Here are some hints: The biggest animals do not live on land as elephants do. They are not extinct (gone) as dinosaurs are. These animals live in the sea, and some of them are living today. Have you guessed the answer yet? Blue whales are the biggest animals that have ever lived on Earth.

Larger Than Large

All whales are big compared to people, but blue whales are huge. A full-grown blue whale can be as long as three school buses parked end to end. And it can weigh as much as 30 elephants put together! Just the heart of a blue whale is as big as a small car. A blue whale can hold enough air in its lungs to stay underwater for almost an hour without taking a breath.

Gentle Giants

You might think that such a huge animal would be scary and dangerous, like the tyrannosaur. But blue whales are really very gentle. Have you ever heard someone say they are afraid of being swallowed by a whale? They shouldn't be. Although a blue whale's body is huge, it can't swallow anything as big as a person. In fact, blue whales eat very tiny shrimp-like animals called *krill.* Krill are from one-half to six inches long.

How can such huge animals stay alive if they eat only tiny sea animals? The answer is, they eat a lot! An adult blue whale eats two tons of krill every day. That's about the same weight as a large pickup truck.

Just Like You!

You might not think whales are much like people. After all, blue whales are huge, and you are not. Blue whales live in the sea, and you live on land. But like people, whales are mammals. Whales have hair on their bodies, though not a lot of hair, as we do. Their babies are born alive as you were born, not hatched from eggs. Mother whales feed their babies milk from their bodies, just as human mothers can give milk to their babies. And all whales breathe air, just as you breathe air.

A Whale of a Problem

Because blue whales are so big, they have no real enemies except people. Until the 1960s, whales were hunted and killed for the oil their bodies contain. Until even more recently, whales were hunted for food. Despite efforts to save them, blue whales are still in danger. They sometimes get caught in fishing nets, many get sick from poisoned water, and they are still hunted, even though such hunting is against the law. So many blue whales have been killed that scientists are worried. They are afraid all blue whales will soon be gone from our planet. If that happens, no one will ever get another chance to see the biggest animal that ever lived. That would be very sad for all of us.

1. How do you think the author feels about people hunting blue whales?

A. sad

B. pleased

C. unsure

D. curious

2. What does the drawing on page 71 show?

A. the height of a blue whale

B. the length of a school bus

C. the length of a blue whale

D. the height of a school bus

3. Under which heading can you find the weight of a blue whale?

A. "Larger Than Large"

B. "Gentle Giants"

C. "Just Like You!"

D. "A Whale of a Problem"

4. A blue whale weighs about as much as

A. a school bus.

B. a small car.

C. 30 elephants.

D. a small pickup truck.

5. If you were going to add information about what is being done to save blue whales, under which heading would you put this information?

A. "Larger Than Large"

B. "Gentle Giants"

C. "Just Like You!"

D. "A Whale of a Problem"

Additional Practice Questions

6. **The writer compares whale mothers to human mothers because whale mothers**

   A. have more than one baby.

   B. rock their babies to sleep.

   C. give their babies milk.

   D. keep their babies safe.

7. **The author MOST LIKELY wrote this passage**

   A. to inform the reader about blue whales.

   B. to teach the reader about shrimp-like krill.

   C. to entertain the reader with a funny story about whales.

   D. to show the reader how whales and elephants are different.

8. **Which two words in the story rhyme?**

   A. sea, breath

   B. air, hair

   C. school, oil

   D. big, huge

Look at the diagram about adult blue whales and adult humans, then answer the question that follows.

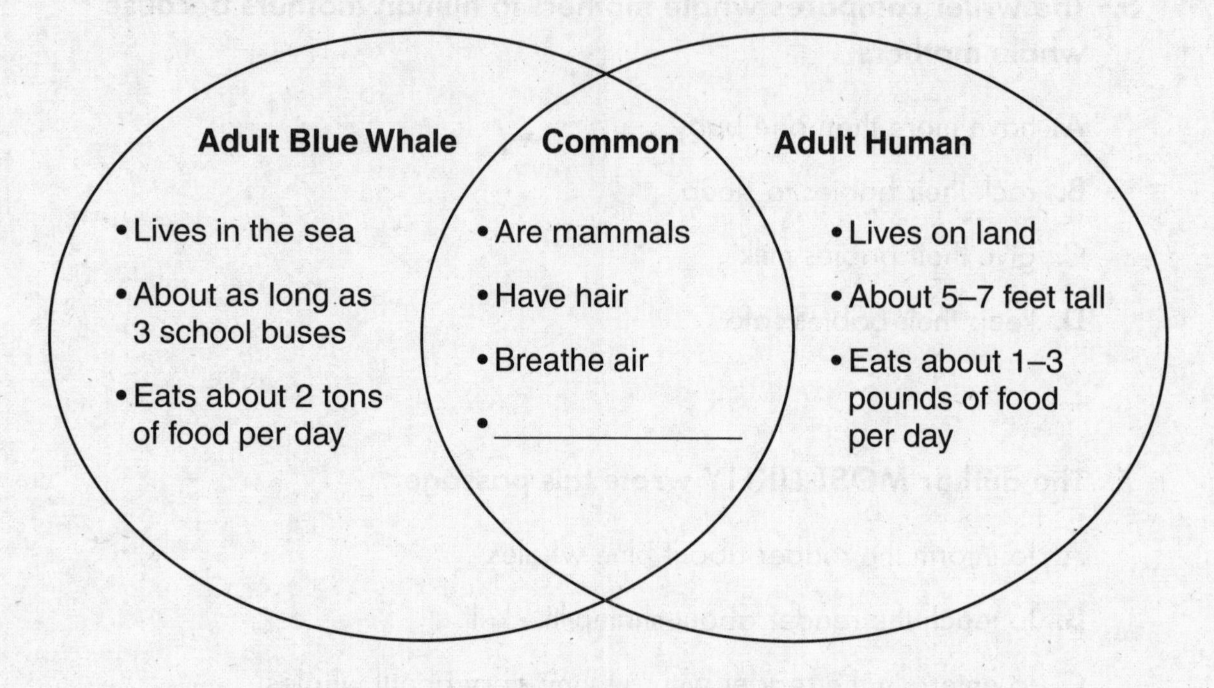

9. Which of the following should be added to the list of things that are common to BOTH?

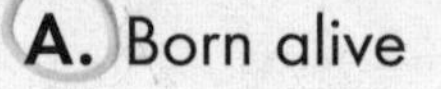

A. Born alive

B. Hunted for food

C. Bigger than dinosaurs

D. Hatched from eggs

Lesson 6

Don't Forget the Details

Read the following story. It will help you learn the tips in this lesson.

Doggone It

by Harriet Rosenbaum

Imagine that your dog, Scooter, ran through the backyard gate when your brother, Olaf, took out the trash yesterday. You really love Scooter. You want her to come home. So you and Olaf (who feels pretty bad that Scooter got away from him) make 10 posters to hang up in your Gainesville neighborhood. This is what the posters look like:

Pretty soon the telephone starts ringing. You quickly pick it up.

"Did you lose a cat?" the caller asks.

"No, we lost our dog," you say.

"Oh, sorry to bother you. I found a lost cat," the caller says and hangs up.

Oops. You and Olaf take markers and run out to add the word dog to all the posters.

An hour later, the phone rings again. "I've found a lost dog that might be yours," the caller says.

"Scooter! You've found Scooter," you say. "Thanks! I really miss my little brown dog."

"Oh, I guess I don't have Scooter," the caller says. "This dog is big and has a red coat. I hope you find your dog." She hangs up.

"Come on, Olaf," you say. "Here we go again." The two of you take your markers and add some more words to the posters.

It's suppertime, and Scooter still hasn't returned home. You're really getting worried now. You walk outside and call, "Scooter! Come home, girl!" No luck. The phone rings, and you rush into the house to answer it.

"Hello, I've found a little brown dog in my yard. I wonder if it could be yours," the caller says. "Does your little brown dog have any markings on her?"

"Yes, she has a white spot on her nose, and the tip of her tail is white," you tell the caller.

"This dog has a white spot on her nose, and the tip of her tail is white," the caller says. "I think I've got your little brown dog. Please come over right away to find out if she is yours."

Your parents drive you and Olaf to the caller's house. There you see that Scooter is tied to a tree with a long leash. "Scooter!" you yell as you run up to hug her.

Scooter gives you a great big lick on your cheek. She's happy to see you, too.

Details Are Important

In the story about Scooter, you and Olaf put up a poster about your lost dog. But there is a problem.

At first, the poster doesn't give much information about Scooter. It doesn't tell that she is a female. It doesn't tell that she is little. It doesn't tell that she is brown. It doesn't even tell that she is a dog. The poster doesn't give any details (information) about the missing dog.

1. Go back to the story and underline details that tell you about Scooter.

2. The poster doesn't tell everything you know about Scooter. Add one more detail about Scooter to the last poster on page 78.

3. Where are Scooter's white spots?
   A. on her back and her front paws
   B. on her nose and the tip of her tail
   C. on all four paws and the tip of her nose
   D. on her belly and her ears

4. What detail is printed on the posters but is not given in the story?
   A. the dog's color
   B. the size of the lost dog
   C. the phone number to call
   D. the dog's markings

5. How does adding details to the poster help in finding Scooter?

____

____

____

____

____

____

TIP 1: Use details to understand the main idea of a story or an information passage.

Details are important in reading passages, just as they are on a "lost dog" poster. They help readers picture what is happening. They help us understand how things are alike and different. They make the characters and events "come alive" for us as we read. Most important, they help us understand the main idea in any kind of writing.

Read the following passage. Then answer Numbers 6 through 11.

> When Mrs. Frederick C. Little's second son arrived, everybody noticed that he was not much bigger than a mouse. The truth of the matter was, the baby looked very much like a mouse in every way. He was only about two inches high; and he had a mouse's sharp nose, a mouse's tail, a mouse's whiskers, and the pleasant, shy manner of a mouse.
>
> —from *Stuart Little* by E. B. White

Fill in the correct details from the passage on the lines below.

6. What is the name of Stuart Little's mother?

____

7. How many older brothers does Stuart have?

____

8. What does everybody think baby Stuart looks like?

____

9. How big is Stuart when he arrives?

____

10. What parts of Stuart look like a mouse?

    his ____

    his ____

    his ____

11. How does Stuart act?

____

____

TIP 2: Find key (important) words in detail questions and answer choices, then look for the same words in the passage.

Most detail questions and answer choices contain important words from the passage. These important words are called **key words.** Key words are clues that can help you find answers in the reading passage. Look for key words in the information passage that follows.

> Imagine that you weighed 85 tons and were about as tall as a four-story building. Would your legs get tired of supporting your heavy body?
>
> Now, imagine the brachiosaur (BRACK-ee-uh-SAWR). Its body was so heavy that it needed gigantic legs just to hold it up. Some scientists have compared the brachiosaur's legs to the pillars that help hold up the roof of a building.

As big and bulky as they were, the legs of the brachiosaur still got extremely tired. That's why the animal spent so much time standing in water. The water helped hold up the brachiosaur's body—and probably soothed those aching legs, too!

Look for the **bold** key words in Numbers 12 through 14. They will help you find the answers to the questions.

12. About how **tall** was a brachiosaur?

____

13. What part of a brachiosaur has been **compared** to the **pillars** that hold up a **building**?

____

14. Why did the brachiosaur spend so much **time** in the **water**?

A. because it got very thirsty
B. because it wanted to hide its big legs
C. because the water helped hold up its body
D. because it liked to stay clean

TIP 3: Retell the story or information in your own words to help put the events in order.

Details tell readers what happens first, second, third, and so on. One of the best ways to keep a story or information straight in your head is to pick out the important details, then retell them in your own words. (Just think about the things you have read and retell them to yourself.)

As you read the following story, look for the most important events.

With a loud crack, Janelle hit the baseball with her new Andruw Jones bat. It sailed high above the torn red cap on Billy Maxwell's head. It grazed the leaves on a branch of the willow tree. Heading straight for Mr. Flannery's house, it slid above the rickety board fence at the edge of Janelle's yard. And it kept going, right through Mr. Flannery's living room window.

Janelle waited for the crash of glass. She waited for an angry yell. But Mr. Flannery didn't get mad.

His window was open! The ball landed on a book in his lap. He stood up, leaned out the window, and threw the ball back over the fence.

15. Underline three important events in the passage.

16. Retell the important events in your own words.

____

____

____

____

____

____

TIP 4: Read all the choices before you choose your final answer.

Just because choice A seems like the correct answer, don't actually choose it until you have carefully read all of the other choices. There could be a better answer in choices B or C. Use this tip to answer Number 17.

Read the chart that follows. It shows the order in which some of the events in the story happened.

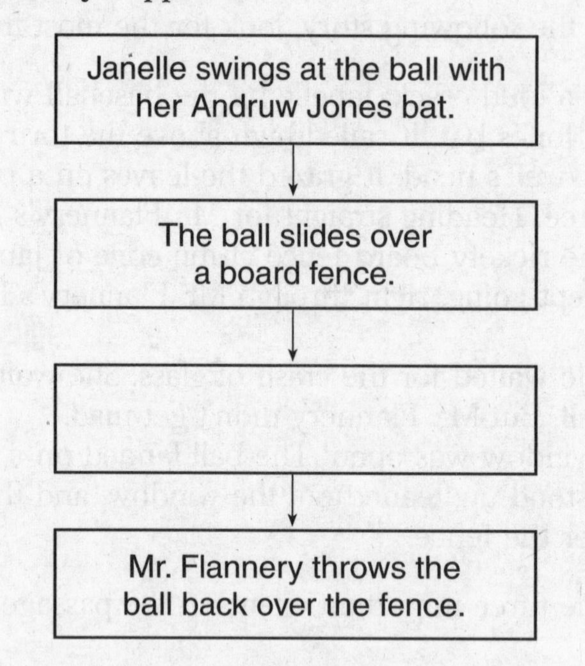

17. Which of these belongs in the empty box?
 A. The ball sails high over Billy Maxwell's head.
 B. The ball heads straight for Billy Maxwell's house.
 C. The ball goes through Mr. Flannery's window and into his lap.
 D. The ball hits the branches of a willow tree.

TIP 5: Look for "order words" such as *first, next,* and *last.*

Sometimes when you read a passage, you will see words that help you know the order in which actions take place. Here are some "order words" to look for:

first	before	following	now	as
next	after	at last	later	during
last	at first	then	while	as soon as

Complete the following sentences using words from the word-order box above.

18. Martin took a nap ________________ Braves-Mets game.

19. Huong washed her hands, ________________ she combed her hair.

20. Diane sang ________________ her brother played the piano.

21. Megan plans to go to Macon ________________.

Don't Forget the Details
Lesson 6 Summary

When answering questions about details and order of events, remember the following tips:

- Use details to understand the main idea of a story or an information passage.
- Find key (important) words in detail questions and answer choices, then look for the same words in the passage.
- Retell the story or information in your own words to help put the events in order.
- Read all the choices before you choose your final answer.
- Look for "order words" such as *first, next,* and *last.*

CRCT Practice

Directions: Read the passage, and then answer the questions.

A Super Idea

by Laura London

1. Jerry met Joe in 1931 while the two boys were in high school. They became best friends and began making comic strips. Jerry wrote the stories, and Joe drew the pictures. They tried to sell their comic strip ideas to local newspapers, but no editors would buy them.

Jerry and Joe did not give up. Nothing could stop these two friends. They kept writing and drawing comics. Soon the two boys started their own magazine, *Science Fiction,* which they printed on a machine at Glenville High School.

One night in 1934, Jerry stayed up all night. He was writing down ideas for a great new comic strip hero. His new strip would mix science fiction with crime solving. Jerry based his character on *Flash Gordon* (a popular comic strip and movie series) and *The Shadow* (a popular crime-fighting program in the early days of radio).

The next morning, Jerry ran 12 blocks to Joe's house. He told his friend about the new character. Joe began to make drawings of their new hero at once.

Although both boys were excited about the character, no one wanted to buy the strip for their newspapers or comic books. But the boys didn't give up. They finished high school and soon found jobs writing and drawing for other comic books. They kept trying to sell their own idea, too.

Finally, Joe and Jerry got their chance. It came from Harry Donenfeld, who was starting a new series of comic books called *Action Comics*. Jerry and Joe sent their new comic strip to Mr. Donenfeld. He liked it.

Mr. Donenfeld sent the boys' comic strip to the editor of *Action Comics*. The editor liked it, too.

It had taken them four years, but in 1938, Jerry Siegel and Joe Schuster finally sold their world-famous comic-book character: Superman!

Sample Detail Questions

1. What year did Jerry and Joe meet?

A. 1931

B. 1934

C. 1935

D. 1938

2. Which event happened FIRST in this passage?

A. Jerry and Joe started their own magazine called *Science Fiction*.

B. Jerry stayed up all night writing down ideas for a new character.

C. Harry Donenfeld started a new set of comic books called *Action Comics*.

D. Jerry and Joe tried to sell their comic strip ideas to local newspapers.

3. What did Jerry do the morning AFTER he stayed up all night?

A. He finished high school.

B. He ran 12 blocks to Joe's house.

C. He started a magazine called *Science Fiction*.

D. He found a job writing and drawing for comic books.

4. Jerry and Joe based their new character on

A. Flash Gordon and Superman.

B. The Shadow and Superman.

C. Flash Gordon and The Shadow.

D. The Shadow and Harry Donenfeld.

5. What did Jerry and Joe do RIGHT AFTER they finished high school?

A. They developed the character of Superman.

B. They found jobs working for other comic books.

C. They sold their Superman comic strip to *Action Comics*.

D. They tried to sell their comic strip ideas to local newspapers.

6. Who FIRST thinks of making a comic strip hero named Superman?

A. Joe Schuster

B. Jerry Siegel

C. Harry Donenfeld

D. the editor of *Action Comics*

Additional Practice Questions

7. Which suffix can you add to the end of the word *excited* to make it mean *in an excited way*?

A. -ful

B. -est

C. -ous

D. -ly

> "Jerry based his character on Flash Gordon (a popular comic strip and movie series) and The Shadow (a popular crime-fighting program in the early days of radio)."

8. The word *popular* means

A. well-liked.

B. polite.

C. soft-spoken.

D. bighearted.

Lesson 7

What's It All About?

Read the following passage. It will help you learn the tips in this lesson.

The Pony Express

by Dexter Evans

In the mid-1800s, there were only two ways to get to California. One way was to sail around the tip of South America. That took a long time. Another way was to cross mountains and deserts on foot and in wagons. Either way, it was a hard and dangerous trip. But, thousands of people moved west anyway. California grew quickly and became a state in 1850.

Frank E. Webner, pictured here about 1861, was one of many young men who rode for the Pony Express.

Because California was far from the rest of the United States, mail service was very slow. It could take months for letters to be delivered. Nobody wanted to wait that long for news about their friends and families far away.

Three men, whose names were William H. Russell, Alexander Majors, and William Waddell, ran a company that carried goods and passengers by wagon and stagecoach. In 1860, they hired a group of young men to ride fast horses from St. Joseph, Missouri, to Sacramento, California. Each rider would carry the mail for about 80 miles, stopping at a relay station every 10 to 15 miles to get a fresh horse. When a rider reached his final stop (called a home station), he would give the mail to another rider, who would carry it 80 miles to the next home station. (It was like a relay race.) This way, the mail could get to and from California much faster. The new mail service was called the Pony Express.

The Pony Express wanted riders who did not have families because the job was so dangerous. The young men rode alone across Indian lands. It was a difficult job, but the mail almost always got through. It took the riders only eight or ten days to go from St. Joseph to Sacramento, instead of many weeks.

After 18 months, telegraph wires finally reached California, making it easier to send and receive messages. The Pony Express went out of business. It has been famous ever since as a colorful part of the history of the Old West.

The Most Important Idea

Everything you read–whether it's a story, a poem, or even a math book–tells you something. That "something" is called the **main idea**. It's what the passage is *mostly* about. Some stories have many important ideas, but there is only one *most* important idea.

Here are some of the important ideas in "The Pony Express":

- The trip west to California was hard and dangerous.
- William H. Russell, Alexander Majors, and William Waddell started a service that carried the mail to and from California.
- Riding for the Pony Express could be a dangerous job.
- The Pony Express ran for only about 18 months.

There is only one *main* idea in the whole story about the Pony Express. The main idea isn't given in a single sentence. You have to put together the details to figure it out.

1. What is the most important idea of the passage?
   A. Pony Express relay stations were about 15 miles apart.
   B. It took a long time to sail around the tip of South America.
   C. The Pony Express cut the time for mail service to and from California.
   D. Telegraph wires put the Pony Express out of business.

2. Go back to the story and underline details that tell about the main idea.

TIP 1: Look for a sentence that tells the main idea.

Sometimes a writer will come right out and tell you the main idea in a sentence.

Spider webs are interesting and unusual things. Most spider webs are sticky because they are used to trap prey. But how do spiders walk on their webs without getting stuck? They have oily feet that slip and slide easily over the silk. If a spider falls backward onto its own web, it will stick there like any other creature. Aargh!

There is a spider in Europe that spins a web so tiny, it's hard to see. It would barely cover a postage stamp.

If you went to India, however, you might see something quite the opposite of such a tiny web. One spider from India builds a web so big that it could cover half your classroom.

The water spider, as you might guess from its name, doesn't mind the water. But before crawling in, it moves its bell-shaped web through the water to collect air bubbles. When it has enough air bubbles, the spider heads below in its own little diving bell to look for food.

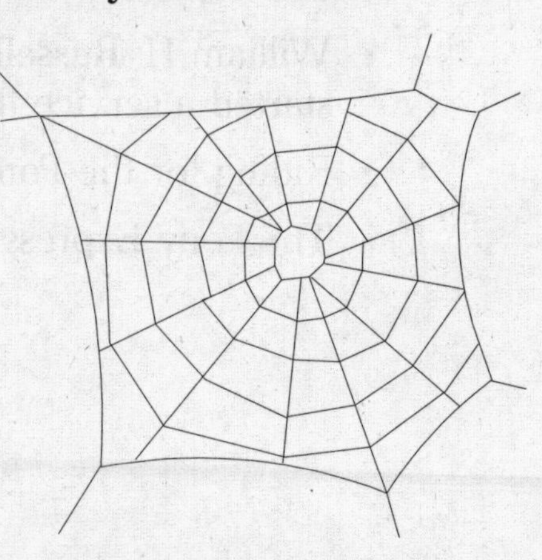

3. What is the main idea of this passage?
   A. Spider webs are interesting and unusual things.
   B. Spiders can walk on their webs without getting stuck.
   C. One spider in Europe spins a web so tiny, it's hard to see.
   D. Water spiders dive under water to look for food.

4. The first paragraph is mostly about
   A. the way spiders walk on their sticky webs.
   B. the tiny web made by a spider from Europe.
   C. the huge web made by an Indian spider.
   D. the way the water spider uses its web to collect air bubbles.

5. The last paragraph is mostly about
   A. the tiny web made by a spider from Europe.
   B. the huge web made by an Indian spider.
   C. the way the water spider uses its web to collect air bubbles.
   D. the way spiders walk on their sticky webs.

TIP 2: Look for details that support the main idea.

Supporting details give important information about the main idea. You could say that they help to "hold up" the main idea. In the passage about spider webs, the main idea is that webs are interesting and unusual. The details tell about interesting and unusual webs.

The next paragraph is from a book about Eleanor Roosevelt. She was a civil rights leader, a writer, a U.S. ambassador to the United Nations, and the wife of President Franklin D. Roosevelt. The paragraph tells what Eleanor and her family saw in London when she was a child.

Eleanor Roosevelt in 1933

Sometimes the people looked strange and exciting. They saw men from Scotland who wore plaid skirts, which Eleanor's father said were called kilts. They saw women from India dressed in yards and yards of beautiful cloth, which her mother said were called saris. In one large building they saw some English judges who wore long black robes and long white wigs that reached to their shoulders.

—from *Eleanor Roosevelt: Fighter for Social Justice*
by Ann Weil

6. What is the main idea of this passage?
   A. Men from Scotland wore plaid skirts called kilts.
   B. Some people looked strange and exciting to Eleanor.
   C. Women wore yards of beautiful cloth called saris.
   D. Some English judges wore long black robes and long white wigs.

7. Look back at the paragraph about Eleanor Roosevelt. Circle two details that support the main idea.

TIP 3: Summarize (retell in a few of your own words) the main idea.

Sometimes a writer just hints at the main idea. If you can't find a main idea sentence, try the following:

- Look for important details in the passage.
- Decide how the details work together.
- In a few of your own words, summarize how the details are connected.

Your sentence should tell how the important ideas work together. The way they work together is what the passage is *mostly* about.

Read the following paragraph, then answer Numbers 8 through 11.

> Freddy Dissel had two problems. One was his older brother, Mike. The other was his younger sister, Ellen. Freddy thought a lot about being the one in the middle. But there was nothing he could do about it. He felt like the peanut butter part of a sandwich, squeezed between Mike and Ellen.
>
> —from *The One in the Middle Is the Green Kangaroo* by Judy Blume

8. What are Freddy Dissel's two problems?

____

9. What does Freddy think about?

____

10. How does Freddy feel?

____

11. Which sentence best summarizes the main idea of the paragraph?
    A. Freddy has a younger sister, Ellen.
    B. Freddy doesn't like being the middle child.
    C. Freddy doesn't like peanut butter sandwiches.
    D. Freddy has a problem with his brother Mike.

TIP 4: The lesson that an important character learns is often the main idea.

You might be asked to show that you understand the main idea or message of a passage by telling about a lesson the main character has learned. Look for a sentence that tells what lesson the character learns. If you can't find a sentence that tells you, put the lesson in your own words. Read the next two paragraphs, then answer Numbers 12 through 14.

Before the trip, Manfred had worried about visiting the United States. His English wasn't the best. And he had never been so far from home before. Now, after spending part of the summer with his cousin in Youngstown, he was on his way back to Germany.

Freddie (as his cousin called him) had learned to enjoy ketchup on his french fries. He had taught himself to ride a bicycle without using his hands. He had learned how to play baseball—and he had given his cousin lessons in soccer. After thinking about it, Manfred didn't know why he had been so worried. He had enjoyed his summer, and he hoped to visit his cousin again.

12. What is the main idea of the first paragraph?

____

____

13. What is the main idea of the second paragraph?

____

____

Now connect the ideas to find what lesson Manfred learns about himself.

14. What is the main lesson that Manfred learns about himself?
    A. that baseball is an easier sport to play than soccer
    B. that he is not afraid to travel and learn new things
    C. that speaking English is not as difficult as he thought
    D. that he was good at riding a bicycle without his hands

TIP 5: To find the main idea, try coming up with a title for the passage.

A good title often tells the reader something about the main idea of the passage. Read the following paragraph. Think about the main idea.

> "Before we go to recess I have something to tell you," Mrs. Lucas began. She was using her serious voice. It was the same one she used when she told them the janitor had died. Everyone was quiet.
>
> —from *Earthquake in the Third Grade* by Laurie Myers

First, read Number 19 on the next page—but don't answer Number 19 until you have answered Numbers 15 through 18.

15. Would Mrs. Lucas use a serious voice to talk about fun at recess?

____

16. Is everyone quiet the whole school day?

____

17. Are the children having recess with Mrs. Lucas right now?

____

18. What voice would Mrs. Lucas use to tell the class bad news?

____

19. Which title best tells about the paragraph?
   A. "A Quiet Day in School"
   B. "Recess with Mrs. Lucas"
   C. "Mrs. Lucas Has Bad News"
   D. "Third-Grade Students"

TIP 6: Remember, main idea questions can be asked in many different ways.

Go back to page 90 and reread "The Pony Express." Then answer some of the different kinds of main idea questions you might see on a reading test.

20. What is the main idea of the passage?
   A. In the mid-1800s, mail delivery to California was very slow.
   B. Californians didn't want to wait months for their mail, so William H. Russell, Alexander Majors, and William Waddell started the Pony Express.
   C. After 18 months, telegraph wires reached California and put the Pony Express out of business.
   D. The Pony Express wanted riders who did not have families because the job was so dangerous.

21. This passage is mostly about
   A. Alexander Majors.
   B. the Pony Express service.
   C. California becoming a state.
   D. traveling in the Old West.

22. Which of the following would be the best title for the passage?
   A. "William Russell and His Wagons"
   B. "The Telegraph Comes to California"
   C. "Relay Racing the Mail to California"
   D. "The New State of California"

23. Which of the following is the best summary of this passage?
   A. In the mid-1800s, there were only two ways to get to California. One was to cross mountains on foot or in wagons. The other was to sail around the tip of South America.
   B. People in California were a long way from the rest of the people in the United States. Because of this, mail could take weeks or months to arrive by usual ways.
   C. To speed up mail delivery to California, three men hired a group of young men to ride fast horses and deliver the mail from St. Joseph, Missouri, to Sacramento, California. The service was called the Pony Express.
   D. When telegraph wires reached California, it became easier to send and receive messages. The new service put the Pony Express out of business.

What's It All About?

Lesson 7 Summary

When answering main idea questions, remember the following tips:

- Look for a sentence that tells the main idea.
- Look for details that support the main idea.
- Summarize (retell in a few of your own words) the main idea.
- The lesson that an important character learns is often the main idea.
- To find the main idea, try coming up with a title for the passages.
- Remember, main idea questions can be asked in many different ways.

CRCT Practice

Directions: Read the passage, then answer the questions.

50%

Silent Music

by Ted Remington

Ludwig von Beethoven was one of history's greatest musicians. He played his first public concert when he was seven years old. He wrote many famous pieces of music. His works are still being played today. What makes Beethoven most unusual is that he wrote much of his greatest music after he lost his hearing.

Ludwig von Beethoven

Before he was 30 years old, Beethoven began to fear that he was going deaf. He was right. Soon, he couldn't hear a thing. It's hard to imagine a greater loss to a musician than the loss of one's hearing. Beethoven was deeply saddened and hurt. He had been one of the best piano players in all of Europe, but his skills had faded with his hearing. Beethoven wondered how he could play and write music if he could not hear.

Even though he was deaf, Beethoven did not feel as though his life's work was finished. Then, he realized something. He could still "see" the sound of music in his mind. Because he could "see" the music in his mind, he could write down the notes and play them as he had done before. The joy of creating made him feel useful again.

One of Beethoven's most famous works is his Ninth Symphony. Hundreds of people came to hear it played for the first time. When it was over, they clapped and cheered. Beethoven didn't know the crowd was cheering until he turned around and saw them. He had created a great work, but he never heard it.

Sample Main Idea Questions

1. What is this passage MOSTLY about?

A. Beethoven's Ninth Symphony

B. the life of Ludwig von Beethoven

C. how to write music when you can't hear

D. learning to play Beethoven's music

2. What is the main idea of the second paragraph?

A. Beethoven is deeply saddened and hurt.

B. Beethoven had been one of the best piano players in Europe.

C. Beethoven becomes deaf and wonders if he can still play and write music.

D. Beethoven is happy that people enjoyed his Ninth Symphony.

3. The last paragraph is MAINLY about

A. the great music that Beethoven wrote before he was 30 years old.

B. the fact that Beethoven could not hear his own music or the cheering crowd.

C. the last symphony that Beethoven wrote.

D. the first concert that Beethoven played when he was seven years old.

4. Which detail from the passage supports the idea that, at FIRST, deafness made Beethoven feel useless?

A. The joy of creating made him feel useful again.

B. A large crowd came to hear his Ninth Symphony.

C. He played his first concert when he was seven years old.

D. His works are still being played today.

5. What makes Beethoven begin to feel that he can still write music, even though he can't hear?

A. He becomes one of the best piano players in all of Europe.

B. He hears the crowd cheering for his Ninth Symphony.

C. He realizes that he can "see" the sound of music in his mind.

D. He plays his first concert when is seven years old.

Additional Practice Questions

"What makes Beethoven most unusual is that he wrote much of his greatest music after he lost his hearing."

6. What does the word *unusual* mean?

A. not usual

B. more usual

C. against usual

D. wrongly usual

> "He had been one of the best piano players in all of Europe, but his skills had faded with his hearing."

7. The word *faded* means

A. taken over.

B. gone away.

C. gotten better.

D. moved up.

8. Which happens FIRST in this passage?

A. Beethoven realizes he can "see" the sound of music in his mind.

B. Beethoven begins to lose his hearing before he turns 30 years old.

C. Beethoven writes his Ninth Symphony and hundreds of people come to hear it.

D. Beethoven doesn't know that the crowd is cheering until he turns around and sees them.

Lesson 8

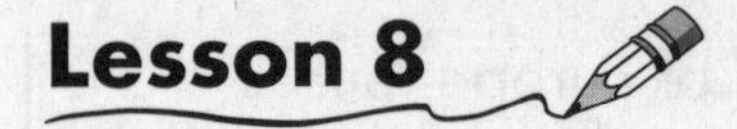

Putting Ideas Together

Usually, just reading a story or poem isn't enough. To understand everything that happens and what it means, you will want to look at all the different parts of a reading passage. You can use the tools in this lesson to help you put ideas together.

Reading with a Plan

In this lesson, you will learn how to **compare** and **contrast** words and ideas. You will learn how to spot the **main problems** in reading passages and how the characters solve those problems. You will learn about **causes** and their **effects.** You will even learn how to guess what a character is going to do next in the story. This is called **predicting.**

As you read the following passage, think about how the writer uses details and ideas to tell a story.

A Bucket of Rubies

by J. M. Wasson

"Rubies!" Caitlin said as she looked at the bucketful of cherries in front of her. "I'm a rich queen with all the rubies in the kingdom piled in front of me." Caitlin had never seen real rubies. But she was sure they must be a deep red like the cherries.

Grandma hollered from the kitchen, "I'll be right out in just one minute, Caitlin. Then we can get started making that cherry pie you love so much."

Tired of waiting, Caitlin picked up four ruby-colored cherries. She popped the first cherry into her mouth. *Mmmm! Delicious,* she thought.

She ate three more cherries, one by one, spitting the seeds into a paper napkin. Two of them were sweet and yummy, just like the first. But the last cherry–Ugh! It tasted funny. She spit it into her napkin. There in the bruised red pulp was a tiny black worm. *Yuck!* thought Caitlin.

"Whatever are you doing, girl?" Grandma asked. "Sneaking a taste behind your grandma's back?" She placed a mixing bowl on the wooden table in front of Caitlin. It was a little more than half full of water.

"Oh, Grandma, it was so gross! I picked up a cherry and bit into a worm!"

"Well, what would you want to go and do a thing like that for?" Grandma asked with a chuckle.

Grandma's eyes twinkle just like the stars, Caitlin thought. *And her laugh sounds like a pretty bell.*

"I don't want to make cherry pie anymore," Caitlin said.

"Why not?" Grandma asked. "I thought you loved cherry pie."

"I do, Grandma," Caitlin said, "but I don't like worms!"

TIP 1: Details can compare feelings, people, or anything else.

In the story you just read, the writer compares many different things. She uses details to show how they are alike or different.

1. To Caitlin, Grandma's laugh sounds like

____

2. What does the writer compare to rubies?

____

TIP 2: Words that compare things show how those things are alike and different.

Any word that describes a thing can become a comparison word by adding suffixes to it. The book you read last week might have been *scary,* but the book you're reading now might be *scarier.* And the book you will read next week might be the *scariest* of them all.

Use the *er* ending when you want the word to mean *more* (bigg**er**, tall**er**, fast**er**, deep**er**, and so on). Use *est* when you want the word to mean *most* (bigg**est**, tall**est**, fast**est**, deep**est**, and so on).

The following table shows some **comparison** words (words that compare two or more things) to look for as you read. Of course, there are many others. Write the missing words in the empty spaces.

Comparison Words

Use When Describing One Thing	Use When Comparing Two Things	Use When Comparing Three or More Things
big	bigger	biggest
kind	kinder	
small		smallest
funny	funnier	funniest

TIP 3: Antonyms (opposite words) show differences.

As you learned in Lesson 3, an antonym is a word that means the opposite of another word. When you look at an elephant, you see an animal that is huge. When you look at a mouse, you see an animal that is tiny. The words *huge* and *tiny* are antonyms. Writers often use antonyms to show differences.

Here are a few antonyms to look for. They will help you see how things are different from each other. Add some of your own opposite pairs at the bottom of this table.

Opposite Pairs

happy	sad
noisy	quiet
grumpy	cheerful
wise	foolish
smooth	rough

Look for opposite words and comparison words as you read the next passage.

Cher was the meanest of the Callahan kids. When she gave Mel and me sour looks, we smiled back at her sweet enough to take the pucker out of a lemon. But it did no good. She was as hateful as she could be. She even pulled the legs off bugs to watch them squirm. We were pretty sure she'd do the same to us if she had half a chance. We tried to be loving to Cher like Ma said we should, but it was real hard. If she hadn't been Ma's best friend's daughter, we wouldn't have tried at all.

Obee, Cher's younger brother, was the nicest of the bunch. (His real name was Obadiah, but when little Shelly was learning to talk, she couldn't say it properly. She called him Obee, and the nickname stuck.) Obee went out of his way to help everyone. Some folks used to say that Obee would never harm any living thing, not even a mosquito or a thistle.

—from *Those Callahans!* by Quincy Lawrence

3. Underline any opposite words or comparison words in the passage you just read.

4. Complete the graphic organizer by writing in details about Cher and Obee.

Cher	Obee

5. Who does the narrator think is the nicest of the Callahan kids?
   A. Cher
   B. Obee
   C. Shelly
   D. Mel

6. Which set of words best compares Cher and Obee?
   A. cruel/kind
   B. mother/son
   C. tallest/shortest
   D. daughter/brother

TIP 4: Find the main problem in the passage.

In made-up stories, there is always at least one **main problem.** There are problems in a lot of real-life stories, too. Sometimes, the problem is stated. Other times, you have to connect the details to figure out what the problem is.

Read the following passage from "What's Your Problem, Kid?" by Julie Render. Look for the main problem as you read.

"Dad! Come quick!" Rufus called from under his covers.

No answer.

He shuddered. *Something is in my closet,* he thought.

"Dad!" he tried again. But again, the house was silent.

Two red lights stared at him. They had to be monster eyes. His teeth chattered at the thought.

Rufus tried to hold his shaking body still. "There's no such thing as monsters," he said. "There's no such thing as monsters. And there are no eyes in my closet."

When he was finally calm, Rufus quietly climbed out of bed. He tiptoed closer to his closet, sure that the red lights would turn out to be a teddy bear's eyes or the shiny red buttons on his cowboy shirt. But they might be monster eyes. It was hard to tell. He would have to turn on the light.

Rufus walked to the light switch by the doorway, feeling braver now that he was taking action. He reached out with his left hand and flipped the switch.

"Hey! Turn that off," a growly voice said. "You're waking me up."

Rufus froze, his hand still on the switch. It was a monster! And it was in his closet!

"DAD, come HELP me!" Rufus screamed.

"Rufus," his dad called from the next room. "Please be quiet. You might wake the monster in your closet."

7. What is Rufus's **main** problem?

____

TIP 5: Look for ways the main character tries to solve the main problem.

In most stories, the main character tries to solve a problem. In this story, Rufus tries two solutions. Look back at the story to find them.

8. What is the first solution Rufus tries?
   A. He calls for his dad.
   B. He yells at the monster.
   C. He looks at the clock by his bed.
   D. He pulls the blanket down so he can see.

Rufus's first solution doesn't work. He has to try something else.

9. What does Rufus do when he gets out of bed?

____

TIP 6: Use a "because" sentence to find a cause and its effect.

The actions in a story usually have effects. When one thing happens, it causes something else to happen. When Dad doesn't answer Rufus's calls at the beginning of the story, Rufus gets more scared. He has to get out of bed to turn on the light.

10. Rufus has to turn on the light because

____

11. Why does Rufus turn on the light?
    A. He is afraid of the dark.
    B. He wants to scare the monster with a bright light.
    C. He wants to make sure there is nothing in his closet.
    D. He wants to show his dad that there is a monster in his closet.

TIP 7: Use a timeline to sort out causes and effects.

Most of the time, it's fairly easy to see what causes something to happen. That's because the two things happen close together in time (and in the story).

If you have trouble figuring out causes and effects, try drawing a timeline of the events. All you need is a simple line, such as the one on the next page. As you read about each event, make a mark on the line to show when it happens in the passage. Then, as you learn about new events, mark their places on the timeline, too.

Read this timeline. One of the events from the story is missing.

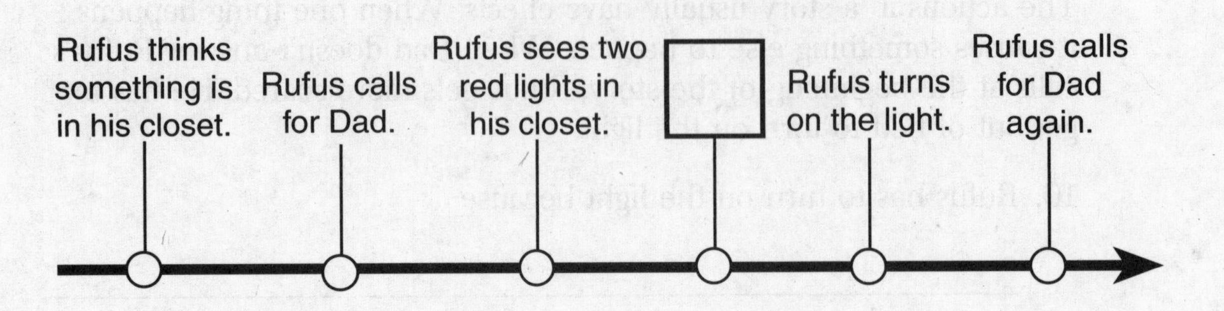

12. Place the letter of the correct event in the empty box on the timeline.
    A. Rufus gets out of bed.
    B. Rufus looks at the clock.
    C. Dad calls from the next room.
    D. The monster growls at Rufus.

TIP 8: Connect the details to get the "whole picture."

Writers don't always tell you everything they're thinking when they write. Sometimes they make you guess. That way, you become more involved with the story. You have to connect the details to get the whole picture. When you connect the details, you fill in the missing blanks using your imagination. This process is called making an **inference.** When reading a passage, you can usually make several inferences to come up with **conclusions** about a character or an event that the author doesn't come right out and tell you. Conclusions are what you learn based on the facts of the passage.

You can make inferences, or **judgments**, about the characters, setting, or events of a story by looking at the details of the story. The details will help you make a conclusion about whether your inferences are correct or incorrect. They act as evidence to either support or disprove an inference.

Sometimes the details of a story will *support* an inference, or *prove* that it is correct. This shows you (or allows you to **conclude**) that your inference was a good one. Sometimes the details of a story will *disprove* an inference. This shows you that your inference was not correct. When the details of a story don't support your inference about that story, you may need to come to a different conclusion.

Read the following passage from *Vinegar Pancakes and Vanishing Cream* by Bonnie Pryor.

> Maybe if I were rich and famous, I wouldn't mind having a name like Martin Elwood Snodgrass. I wouldn't even mind having red hair, about a million freckles, and being the shortest kid in Mrs. Robbin's third grade . . .
>
> I think I will change my name when I grow up. Something like John Smith or Bill Brown would be nice. Martin Elwood Snodgrass sounds like something you would say if you shut your finger in a door and your mother was standing next to you.

Think about the passage you have just read. When the narrator says, "Maybe if I were rich and famous, I wouldn't mind having a name like Martin Elwood Snodgrass," what does he really mean? Let's look at the other details we know:

- The narrator says that none of his problems would really matter if he were rich and famous.
- The narrator thinks he might change his name when he grows up.

By connecting these details, we can make a guess about what the narrator really means. When he says, "Maybe if I were rich and famous, I wouldn't mind having a name like Martin Elwood Snodgrass," the narrator means that, right now, he doesn't like his name.

Sure, the narrator could have come right out and said, "I do not like my name." But the writer knows that you can draw your own **conclusions** (what you learn based on facts in the passage).

TIP 9: Use what you already know from the story to guess what is going to happen next (make a prediction).

When you read a story, you get to know the characters. Sometimes you know them so well that you can **predict** (know ahead of time) what they might do next.

Think about Martin Elwood Snodgrass in the story you just read. He seems to be pretty upset about his name, his freckles, his red hair, and even his height. Can you predict how Martin would feel in another situation? Let's give it a try.

13. When someone teases him about his name, what will Martin MOST LIKELY do?

    A. become angry and start a fight
    B. become close friends with that person
    C. fill with pride because of his fine name
    D. say that he doesn't like his name either

We know that Martin doesn't like his name either (D). Chances are, Martin wouldn't fill with pride because of his name (C), try to make friends with the person teasing him (B), or start a fight (A).

Of course, we can't know for sure unless the writer tells us. But we can use our imaginations to figure things out. Kind of fun, isn't it?

Putting Ideas Together
Lesson 8 Summary

When answering cause-and-effect, compare/contrast, and prediction questions, remember these tips:

- Details can compare feelings, people, or anything else.
- Words that compare things show how those things are alike and different.
- Antonyms (opposite words) show differences.
- Find the main problem in the passage.
- Look for ways the main character tries to solve the main problem.
- Use a "because" sentence to find a cause and its effect.
- Use a timeline to sort out causes and effects.
- Connect the details to get the "whole picture."
- Use what you already know from the story to guess what is going to happen next (make a prediction).

CRCT Practice

Directions: Read the passage, then answer the questions.

A First Time for Everything

by Brian O'Sullivan

When I was eight, Mom and I moved from Waycross to Albany. The good part was that my grandparents lived in Albany. And the bad part? You guessed it. I was about to be "the new kid" in school.

I remember the morning Grandpa drove me to my new school for the first time. I was so scared, my stomach was doing flips. Would my teacher be nice? Would I make friends? Would everyone be ahead of me in math? I could hardly pay attention to Grandpa.

On the way, Grandpa asked, "Did I ever tell you about the first time I flew a kite, Brian?"

I shook my head.

"When I was a little kid–a couple years younger than you are now–my father told me we were going to fly a kite the next day. I was never more scared in my life!"

"Why would you be scared to fly a kite, Grandpa?"

"My dad was a pilot, so I figured a kite must be sort of like an airplane. I thought you had to ride on it to fly it."

"That's pretty funny, Grandpa!"

"Maybe so," Grandpa said, "but that's what I thought. I told my dad I didn't know how to fly a kite. I asked if he'd fly it with me."

"What did your dad say?" I asked.

"He said, 'Son, it's easy to fly a kite. Anyone can do it. Don't worry, I'll help you get the kite up in the air. Then you can fly it all by yourself.' What do you suppose I was thinking about all that night?" Grandpa asked.

"What it would be like to fly a kite?" I asked.

"No, I kept hoping it would rain! But when morning came, it was bright and sunny."

"Then what happened?" I asked.

"The next day, my dad brought out a big piece of paper that was stretched tight over some sticks. It had a long string tied to it. I was really confused then," Grandpa said. "I asked my dad, 'How am I supposed to ride on that little thing?'"

"What did he say?" I asked.

Grandpa laughed at the memory. "My dad was really surprised by what I had asked. I know he was trying hard not to laugh.

"Well, we went to a great big park. Dad showed me how to fly a kite, all right! Boy, did I feel silly when I found out that you fly a kite while you stand on the ground! Because I didn't know what a kite was, I had imagined it to be something scary. Flying a kite turned out to be safe and a lot of fun."

Why is he telling me this now? I wondered.

The car pulled up in front of Lake Park Elementary School on Meadowlark Drive, and Grandpa opened the door to let me out.

"Say, Brian," he said. "When you walk in the door of your new class, just remember what I told you about the kite, okay?"

"Sure, Grandpa," I said. "Thanks for the ride. And thanks for telling me the story." I slipped my arms through the straps of my backpack and walked up the sidewalk to my new school.

Grandpa waved as he drove away.

Now what was that all about? I wondered.

But as I walked through the door, I felt ready for anything. Know what I mean?

Sample Putting Ideas Together Questions

1. How does Brian feel about his new school at the end of the story?

A. worried

B. excited

C. afraid

D. sad

2. What is the main idea of the story Grandpa tells Brian?

A. Sometimes flying a kite can be difficult.

B. If you hope it will rain, it probably won't.

C. Listening to the stories adults tell is important.

D. Things you're not used to can seem scary at first.

3. Why does Grandpa tell Brian the kite story on the way to school?

A. to teach Brian that flying kites is fun

B. to let Brian know that new experiences can be fun

C. to remind himself of how it feels to be young

D. to scold Brian for being afraid to go to his new school

4. Which of the following events happens FIRST?

A. Brian rides to school with Grandpa.

B. Brian gets out of the car at Lake Park Elementary School.

C. Brian walks into the school feeling ready for anything.

D. Brian moves from Waycross to Albany.

5. Which will Brian MOST LIKELY do on his first day of school?

A. ask the principal if he can go home early

B. get angry and not talk to anyone

C. cry outside the doorway to his classroom

D. try to make friends and get to know people

6. What will Brian MOST LIKELY do after school?

A. tell Grandpa about his first day at his new school

B. go to the park with Grandpa to fly a kite

C. teach his new friends about flying kites

D. write a story about going to a new school

Additional Practice Questions

7. Which word BEST describes Grandpa?

A. lonely

B. angry

C. scared

D. caring

8. Which of the following happens just BEFORE Brian walks into the school?

A. Grandpa waves to Brian and drives away.

B. Grandpa tells Brian a story about flying kites.

C. Brian worries that students may be ahead of him in math.

D. Brian worries about his first day at school.

9. Which word from the story has three syllables?

A. something

B. memory

C. backpack

D. scary

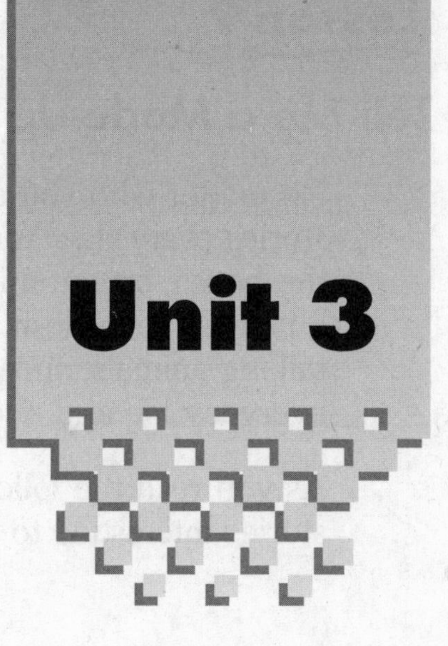

Kinds of Reading

There are all kinds of bicycles, each built for a different purpose, and there are all kinds of writings, each kind having a special purpose of its own.

When you read a work of fiction (a made-up story), you get to "jump into" another world.

Poetry is a special kind of writing that tells about common things in new ways.

Then, there is nonfiction, which tells about real times, real places, and real people.

Are you ready to read? OK, then. Let's go.

In This Unit

- Tell Me a Made-Up Story
- Tell Me a True Story
- Stories for the Stage
- Words That Sing
- Comparing Stories
- Reading Pictures

Lesson 9

Tell Me a Made-Up Story

No matter who you are, chances are good that you come across stories every day. You might tell your friends about a trip you took to the beach, or you might make them laugh with a made-up story about a bear in your closet. Made-up stories can be about other worlds, talking animals, and all kinds of new things. They can also be about everyday life and about people just like you and me.

As you read the following passage, think about what makes made-up stories interesting to read, hear, and even tell.

A Ghost Story?

The pine trees, dark against the rising moon, whispered softly. The girls sat huddled in warm blankets, waiting for Rachel, their counselor, to begin a ghost story. Puffs of wind played with the campfire, swirling sparks up into the night sky. The flames danced. The girls grew very quiet–and Rachel began in a low voice.

"Once upon a time, there were some people who lived somewhere. A ghost scared them."

Rachel had finished her story. Standing up, she brushed the sand from her pants. "Okay, girls. Time for bed," she said.

"Come on!" Karen said. "That was no story! We don't know anything about the people. Tell us about the *characters*."

"Yeah," her friend Heather said. "And we don't know where it happened or when it happened. Tell us about the *setting*."

"We don't even know what happened," Marsha said, sounding disappointed. "Tell us about the *plot*."

Two Kinds of Stories

There are two main **genres**, or kinds, of stories. First, there are stories that are made up by the author. We call this kind of writing **fiction.** You will learn about fiction in this lesson. Second, there are true stories about real people and real things that happen. We call this kind of writing **nonfiction.** You will learn about nonfiction in Lesson 10.

TIP 1: There are many different kinds of fiction.

Here is a list of many different forms of fiction. Most of the examples are probably available in your school or local library. Some books can belong in more than one type of fiction. An adventure story might also be historical fiction, for example.

On the line that follows each kind of fiction, write the name of a story or book–of that kind–that you've read or want to read.

Adventure stories tell about people facing danger or taking some kind of risk. (An example is *Way Home* by Libby Hamilton and Gregory Rogers.)

____

Fantasy stories tell about things that can't happen in real life. They usually have strange settings and even stranger characters. Fantasies include ghost stories and stories about magic. (An example is *The BFG* by Roald Dahl.)

____

Folktales are stories that have been handed down for hundreds of years. They include fairy tales, myths, legends, and fables. (Examples are fairy tales such as "Snow White," myths about Hercules, legends about Paul Bunyan, and fables such as "The City Mouse and the Country Mouse.")

____

Historical fiction tells made-up stories based on real people and real events from history. (*Samantha: An American Girl* by Susan S. Adler is historical fiction.)

Mystery stories tell about solving a crime or a puzzle. (An example is *Nate the Great and the Stolen Base* by Marjorie Sharmat.)

Poetry tells stories or expresses feelings using verse. (Examples can be found in *A Pizza the Size of the Sun* by Jack Prelutsky.)

Realistic fiction tells made-up stories about things that could happen in everyday life. (An example of realistic fiction is *Henry Huggins* by Beverly Cleary.)

Science-fiction stories tell about people using science or inventions, and are usually set in the future. (An example is *Space Dog Hero* by Natalie Standiford.)

TIP 2: A made-up story has characters, a setting, and a plot.

No matter what kind of fiction you are reading, it will always have **characters.** Usually, the characters are people, but they can be animals (such as Bambi or the three little pigs), monsters (such as vampires), and strange creatures (such as Dr. Seuss's Grinch or Aladdin's genie). They can even be trees, cars, or trains that talk. (Do you remember *The Little Engine That Could* by Watty Piper?)

Stories also tell about a **setting**, which is a place and time for the story to happen. The setting might be on a sailing ship, in the mountains, at a ballpark–or even on the moon. The story might take place today, 2,000 years in the past, or sometime far into the future.

Things have to happen in a story, too. These events (happenings) are called the story's **plot**.

Read the following sentences. Then circle the word that tells whether the sentence is *mostly* about characters, setting, or plot.

1. Ten-year-old Randy has a cousin, Louise.
   characters setting plot

2. A bicycle is left unlocked and gets stolen.
   characters setting plot

3. The floor of the cave is cold, and its walls are wet.
   characters setting plot

4. The lake looks like a mirror in the moonlight.
   characters setting plot

5. Describe the setting, characters, or plot of one of your favorite stories.

____

____

____

TIP 3: Get to know the characters through details.

You can get to know the characters in a story if you pay attention to details. You can learn what the characters look like, how they think, and how they act. You may find out whether they are old, young, kind, mean, happy, or sad. You will find out if they are boys or girls, men or women, dogs or cows, talking trees or singing airplanes, and so on.

Read this passage from a mystery story. Pay close attention to the details. Then answer Numbers 6 through 10.

Jody ran down the bike path beside Jackson Highway. She was frightened. Her long black hair streamed in the wind. A bright red book bag flopped wildly on her back. Her unbuttoned raincoat flapped in the wind like the wings of a giant yellow bird. When she got to Oak Street, she cut through Mr. Henderson's lawn. Every now and then, she looked over her shoulder to see if Mrs. Parker was still following her.

Jody didn't stop running until she reached Elm Street and the safety of her own front steps. Nearly out of breath, she sat down, flipped the book bag onto her knees, and searched for a pencil. Not finding the pencil, she settled for a stubby green crayon and ripped a page from her third-grade spelling book. With shaking hands, she scribbled a quick note.

> Michelle,
>
> I can't meet you here after school today. I have to do something very important. See you tomorrow—I hope!
>
> Jody C.

6. Which of the following BEST describes Jody?
   A. a private detective
   B. a neighborhood bully
   C. a third-grade student
   D. a friend of Mrs. Parker

7. Where does Jody live?
   A. on Elm Street
   B. on Oak Street
   C. near a bike path
   D. along Jackson Highway

8. Which word BEST tells how Jody feels?
   A. angry
   B. fearful
   C. cheerful
   D. grouchy

9. The author MOST LIKELY wants readers to feel
   A. sad
   B. joyful
   C. amazed
   D. worried

10. In your own words, tell how Jody is dressed and what she looks like.

____

____

____

____

TIP 4: Use details to picture the setting.

The story's **setting** is the time and place an action happens. Longer stories and books may have many different settings. Again, look for details. They will tell you when and where the story takes place.

Read this historical fiction passage, then answer Numbers 11 through 13.

It was New Year's Eve, 1818. Captain Henry stood at the wheel of his steamboat, the *City of Savannah*, which was headed down river from Augusta. From the wheelhouse atop his boat, he peered down the moonlit Savanna River. He watched carefully for shallow waters, sandbars, and tree snags.

Bright sparks and heavy black smoke poured out of the boat's tall smokestacks. The soot-filled clouds trailed upriver and floated on the still night air. Steam hissed from the boilers. And softly, the tinkle of a piano drifted up from the carpeted main cabin.

She's making good time, the captain thought. *We should be in Savannah before midnight.*

11. Which words BEST describe the setting?
   A. clear and windy
   B. cloudy and windy
   C. moonlit and still
   D. cloudy and still

12. Which words BEST describe the setting of this passage?
   A. in Savannah, Georgia
   B. aboard a Savannah River steamboat
   C. near some sandbars and tree snags
   D. near the piano in a carpeted main cabin

13. What time of year does the action take place?
   A. summer
   B. fall
   C. winter
   D. spring

TIP 5: Find the problems to learn about the plot.

Stories wouldn't be very interesting without plots. Most of the time, the plot is about **problems** the characters face. These problems make the story exciting.

Most stories have a **main problem** and other, smaller problems. The main character may have a problem with another character, such as a parent, a neighbor, or a teacher. Or, the problem might be with a thing, such as a storm, a wild animal, or a broken bicycle.

Sometimes, the problem will be within the character. *Should I do this, or should I do that?* the character will wonder. Usually these problems will develop around the main idea of the story.

TIP 6: Try to predict (guess) what will happen later in the story.

When you try to guess what will happen next in a story, you are making a **prediction**. To make a good prediction, use clues from the story, things you have learned in your own life, and your common sense. Making predictions as you read will help you understand the story better and enjoy it more–even if your predictions aren't right.

Read each paragraph and predict what will happen next.

14. Josh and Courtney finished spooning a batch of chocolate chip cookies onto a cookie sheet. Putting their cookies into a hot oven, they rushed outside to play for 10 minutes while the cookies baked. They didn't set a timer or take a watch with them.

    a. Predict what will happen next.

    ____

    ____

They laughed and played for 25 minutes before Courtney suddenly remembered the cookies. When they looked up, they saw clouds of smoke rolling from the kitchen window.

b. Was your prediction for Number 14a correct?

❑ Yes ❑ No

c. Predict what Josh and Courtney will do now.

____

____

____

15. Martin decided to take a shortcut through Mr. Johnson's pasture. He had forgotten about Mr. Johnson's large bull.

a. Predict what will happen next.

____

____

The large animal pawed the ground, then lowered its head and began to chase the boy. Running as fast as he could, Martin looked up and saw a large oak tree near the pasture's edge.

b. Was your prediction for Number 15a correct?

❑ Yes ❑ No

c. Predict what Martin will do now.

____

____

TIP 7: Most stories follow a set pattern.

Most stories follow a pattern like this:

The **beginning** of a story tells about the characters and the setting. It also tells about the problems faced by the main character or characters.

The middle, or **body**, of a story tells how the characters' problems get bigger and bigger. The problems continue to grow until the story reaches its **climax.** The climax is the point in the story where the problems stop getting bigger and start to be solved. Either that, or the characters start learning how to live with their problems.

The **end** of a story tells how the problem is solved or the characters accept their problems and adjust to them. This is called the problem's **resolution.**

16. Think of a fairy tale you know (such as "Cinderella," "Snow White," "Goldilocks and the Three Bears," "Hansel and Gretel," "The Three Billy Goats Gruff," "Little Red Riding Hood," "The Ugly Duckling," "The Princess and the Pea," or any other fairy tale you know and like). Then answer the following questions about it.

    a. Which fairy tale have you selected?

    ____

    b. What do you learn about the characters, settings, and characters' problems at the beginning of the fairy tale?

    ____

    ____

    ____

c. What happens during the middle of the story? How do the problems get bigger for the main character?

____

____

____

____

d. How does the story end? How are the problems solved?

____

____

____

____

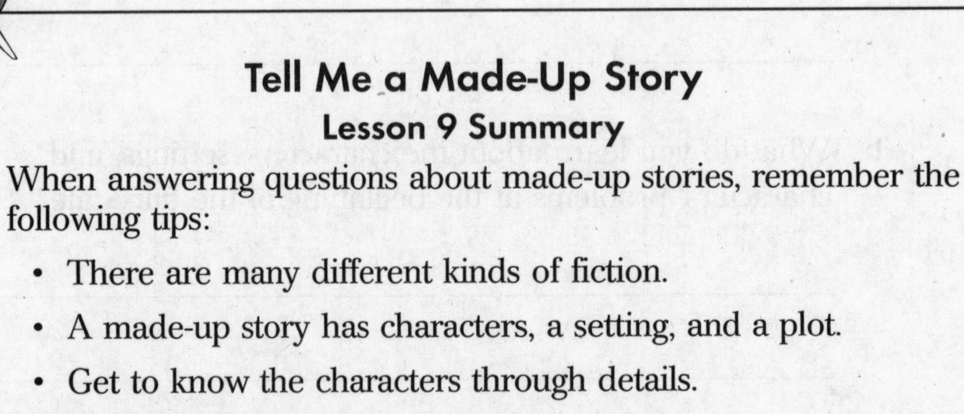

Tell Me a Made-Up Story

Lesson 9 Summary

When answering questions about made-up stories, remember the following tips:

- There are many different kinds of fiction.
- A made-up story has characters, a setting, and a plot.
- Get to know the characters through details.
- Use details to picture the setting.
- Find the problems to learn about the plot.
- Try to predict (guess) what will happen later in the story.
- Most stories follow a set pattern.

CRCT Practice

Directions: Read the passage, then answer the questions.

from

The Secrets of the Old Barn

by Robyn Winchell

Uncle Roberto said it would be the perfect way to spend a rainy afternoon. Angie and Rosa agreed. Their aunt and uncle's old barn hadn't been used for years, but the roof was good, and it didn't leak. Although it might be a little dusty, playing in the hayloft would be more fun than staying in the farmhouse for yet another rainy day.

The girls climbed toward the opening in the hayloft floor above them. They could hear the patter of rain peppering the roof and the low rumble of thunder in the distance. Pigeons cooed softly from the shadowy rafters high above them.

"This will be fun," Angie said as her head appeared above the loft floor. She scrambled to her feet in the dusty hay. Rosa followed her sister into the loft like a shadow.

"We can pretend we're mountain climbers," Rosa said, looking at the mounds of hay.

Just then, both girls froze. Something dark and furry hurried across the floor in front of them and disappeared into the hay.

"What was that?" Angie asked.

"Why, it looked like Beanie, Aunt Carmen's cat," Rosa said. "Aunt Carmen says she hasn't seen Beanie for more than two weeks."

"There she is again," Angie said, pointing to the cat, which was now lying on top of the straw, flicking its black tail from side to side.

The girls struggled over piles of loose hay, then bent down to pet the cat. It began to purr loudly. After a few minutes, Beanie stood, stretched, and disappeared into the hay once again. The girls began to hear soft noises coming from under the hay.

"What's making those sounds?" Angie asked.

"I don't know," Rosa replied.

The girls waited quietly, listening to the soft sounds coming from the hay. In a very short time, Beanie came back out. This time she was carrying a small spotted kitten in her mouth.

"Beanie's had kittens!" Angie said. "And look!" She pointed to a small tunnel in the hay. Four more blue-eyed kittens wobbled toward the girls.

"Oh, they're so cute!" Rosa said. She carefully picked up the littlest one. It squirmed in her hand and mewed a tiny cry.

Beanie gave a warning meow and batted at Rosa's hand with one paw.

"I think you'd better put it down," Angie said. "It doesn't look like Beanie thinks they're ready for company yet. Let's come back later and bring her a saucer of milk."

"Good idea," Rosa said, placing the baby kitten next to its mother.

"See you later, Beanie's babies," Angie said with a smile.

Sample Made-Up Story Questions

1. Why do the girls play in the barn?

A. They are looking for Beanie.

B. They are looking for something new to do.

C. They are tired of playing outside in the rain.

D. They are hoping to see Beanie's kittens.

2. Why do the girls wait quietly when Beanie disappears into the hay for the LAST time?

A. They are worried about climbing back down the ladder.

B. They want to find out what is causing noises in the hay.

C. They don't want to go back outside because it is still raining.

D. They think Beanie may need help finding her way out of the hay.

3. Which of the following BEST describes this passage?

A. fiction

B. nonfiction

C. drama

D. poetry

4. What will MOST LIKELY happen next?

A. Aunt Carmen will tell the girls to clean the barn.

B. The girls will decide to play outside in the rain.

C. The girls will tell their aunt and uncle about the kittens.

D. Uncle Roberto will say that the hayloft is not a safe place to play.

5. **Which word BEST describes the setting of this story?**

   A. a treehouse

   B. a cabin

   C. a farm

   D. a mountain

Additional Practice Questions

6. **The author MOST LIKELY includes the illustrations in this story**

   A. to help the reader follow the plot.

   B. to help the reader picture the characters and setting.

   C. to help the reader picture Beanie and her five kittens.

   D. to show the reader what Uncle Roberto and Aunt Carmen look like.

7. **Which happens FIRST in this story?**

   A. Rosa says the girls should pretend to be mountain climbing.

   B. The girls climb the ladder toward an opening in the hayloft.

   C. Uncle Roberto says the hayloft would be fun on a rainy day.

   D. Four of Beanie's blue-eyed kittens wobble out from beneath the hay.

Lesson 10

Tell Me a True Story

As you learned in Lesson 9, there are many different kinds of made-up stories. Even though true stories are always about real people and places, they come in many forms, too.

As you read the following passage, think about how a true story can be just as interesting and have just as many details as a made-up story.

Books for Boys and Girls

by Alan Noble

In 1922, not long after Beverly Bunn's sixth birthday, her father quit farming. The family moved into a city neighborhood full of children. Beverly loved the city. She loved the neighborhood children. Most of all, she came to love the city's library.

Beverly's father took a job as a bank guard, but he did not make much money. The Bunn family was poor, and their house was cold. Beverly began to spend a lot of time in the warm, comfortable library. The little girl loved to read. When she read mysteries, fairy tales, and biographies of famous people, she didn't have to think about being poor or cold.

Beverly also began to write. When she was in third grade, a local newspaper printed something she had written. It was an article about a book called *The Story of Dr. Doolittle.* In fourth grade, Beverly won a writing contest. By the time she was in high school, she was writing stories for her school newspaper.

When Beverly was 24 years old, she married Clarence Cleary. He thought she would be very good at writing for children. So, Beverly sat down with a box full of sharp pencils and a stack of paper. She wrote a funny book about being a child on Klickitat Street in the city of Portland, Oregon. She said the book was written about ordinary boys and girls. She called it *Henry Huggins.*

That was only the beginning of Beverly Cleary's long writing career. Over the years, she wrote more than 70 books for young people. Beezus, Ramona, and Henry have become favorite friends to countless children all over the world. And it all began with Beverly's trips to the library.

Writing About Real People, Places, and Things

Many stories, poems, and plays tell about things made up by the author. But there are other kinds of writing that tell true stories about real people, real places, real things, and real happenings. You can find true stories in newspapers, magazines, books, and even on the Internet. Writing that is about real things is called nonfiction.

TIP 1: Any story or article about things not made up by the author is called nonfiction.

The passage you just read, "Books for Boys and Girls," is a true story about Beverly Cleary. The passage you read on pages 45 and 46, "The First Brothers of Flight," is also a true story about the Montgolfier brothers and their hot air balloons. History books, geography books, and newspaper articles are all examples of nonfiction. Even some poems (such as "Paul Revere's Ride") deal with real people and real events and can be considered nonfiction.

The following list tells you about some of the most common kinds of nonfiction. As you can tell from reading the list, reading material is everywhere.

Books: Libraries contain thousands of nonfiction books. These books may tell about a single topic, such as making paper airplanes. Or they may tell about a wider variety of topics, such as games and crafts around the world. History, science, math, and stories about people's lives (**biographies** and **autobiographies**) are all nonfiction.

Editorials: Editorials tell how someone feels or thinks. They give facts that support how the writer feels. They are usually written to persuade the reader. Sometimes these are articles, but other times they are letters sent to a newspaper or magazine.

Encyclopedias: There are usually several books in a set. They tell a little bit about every subject you can think of. The topics are listed in alphabetical order.

Magazines: You can find a magazine about almost any subject. Magazine articles usually tell about interesting places, people, events, styles, or products. (Some magazines also contain fictional stories or poems.)

Newspapers: Newspaper articles are true stories about events that have just happened.

Newsletters: These are short (usually four to eight pages) newspapers published by clubs, companies, and groups to keep their members or workers informed.

Instructions: These are written directions to help people do things like fix a bike or set up a computer. A **recipe** is a special set of instructions for preparing a certain kind of food.

The Internet: When you use a computer to get on the Internet, you can find an amazing amount of information. Most of it is nonfiction. But be careful! Anyone around the world can put information on the Internet. Not everything is correct. If you research a topic on the Internet, be sure to use trusted websites and look it up in books you can trust, too.

1. Which of the following books is fiction?
   A. *The Life of Abraham Lincoln*
   B. *The Dragon Under Johnny's Bed*
   C. *Webster's New World Dictionary*
   D. *A History of America's Space Program*

2. Which of the following books is nonfiction?
   A. *Alice in Wonderland*
   B. *Jack and the Magic Beanstalk*
   C. *How Clouds Are Formed*
   D. *Aladdin and His Magical Lamp*

TIP 2: Biographies and autobiographies are true stories about people's lives.

There are two kinds of true stories about people's lives: biographies and autobiographies.

A **biography** is a true story about a person's life written by another person. People who write biographies don't usually talk about themselves in the writing.

An **autobiography** is a true story about the writer's own life. Anyone can write an autobiography. Autobiographies are often called **memoirs** (MEM-wahrs).

Circle the correct answer for Number 3, then answer Number 4.

3. "Books for Boys and Girls," the passage about Beverly Cleary, is which kind of writing?

    an autobiography   a biography

4. How do you know?

    ____

    ____

    ____

TIP 3: Writers always have a purpose for their writing.

Writers always have a **purpose**, or a reason, for writing. We can figure out the writer's purpose by paying close attention to clues in the reading passage.

Most made-up stories, plays, and poems are written to entertain the reader. But nonfiction is written for many different reasons. It may provide information to the reader. It may try to persuade the reader to do or believe in something. It may teach the reader something. Sometimes, like fiction, it is written to entertain. Here are some reasons for writing nonfiction:

Writing to provide information: newspaper articles, magazine articles, and newsletters

Writing to persuade: newspaper ads, magazine ads, editorials, and requests for support from charity organizations

Writing to teach: schoolbooks, how-to books, and directions

Writing to entertain: books about hobbies and travel stories

TIP 4: A fact can be checked to see if it is correct. An opinion cannot be checked.

When people make **fact** statements, they're saying, "This is true. Go ahead and check it out if you don't think it's correct."

If your friend Mickey says, "My bicycle is blue," he's making a statement of fact. You can check the color of his bicycle. Remember, a fact statement may not be true, but it has to be a statement that can be checked. Statements of fact use words that mean the same thing to everybody: *brown, round, square, north, up,* and *down,* for example.

An **opinion** statement cannot be checked. Mickey might say, "My bicycle is fast." How fast? Faster than your bicycle? Faster than a race car? Faster than an airplane? To *him* it might be fast, but to you it might seem slow. Judgment words, such as *better, worse, beautiful, ugly, fast,* and *slow,* are opinion words; they cannot be checked because they mean different things to different people. Remember, an opinion statement uses words that mean different things to different people.

TIP 5: Use clues and details from the story or passage to support your answers to reading questions.

Just as in fiction passages, nonfiction passages support their main ideas with lots of details. You can use those details to come up with your own idea about what's going on in the passage. Look back at the "Books for Boys and Girls" passage on pages 138 and 139 to answer the following questions.

5. What is the main idea of the passage?

____

____

____

____

____

____

____

6. List at least four details that support the passage's main idea.

TIP 6: When reading information passages, ask yourself questions such as Who? What? When? Where? Why? and How?

Newspaper and television reporters use these six questions to make sure they get all the information needed to report the whole story. You can ask yourself the same six questions when reading a passage or article. Answers to such questions will help you to better understand what you are reading.

Newspaper articles are meant to contain only facts and to provide the reader with information. Read the following news story and answer Numbers 7 through 10.

Local school to host noted children's poet

Jennifer Red Bird, noted children's poet, will read from her new book Tuesday afternoon at Kennedy Elementary School and Tuesday evening at the city library. The Native American poet will appear at 2 P.M. in the school library and at 7 P.M. in the city library. She will read from *Coyote Dawn*, a collection of 31 poems, which was published this year.

The public is invited to both readings, but because of limited seating at the Kennedy School library, persons are asked to reserve space by calling the library in advance.

Miss Red Bird has published three earlier books of poetry: *Strawberry Mesa* in 1986, *Cinnamon Town* in 1990, and *Apache Sunrise* in 2002. She is a graduate of Valdosta State College and the University of Georgia. The poet currently teaches English at Oakwood High School in Marietta.

7. When will Jennifer Red Bird read from her new book of poetry?
   A. Tuesday afternoon
   B. Tuesday evening
   C. Tuesday morning
   D. Tuesday afternoon and evening

8. What time will Jennifer Red Bird read for the students of Kennedy Elementary school?
   A. 1 P.M.
   B. 2 P.M.
   C. 2:30 P.M.
   D. 9 P.M.

9. Why must the public make reservations to attend the 2 P.M. reading?
   A. Jennifer Red Bird wants to know how many people are coming.
   B. An exact count is needed in case the library plans to serve treats.
   C. There are only a limited number of seats available in the library.
   D. Jennifer Red Bird wants to know who is coming ahead of time.

10. What did Jennifer Red Bird name her first book of poetry?
   A. *Strawberry Mesa*
   B. *Coyote Dawn*
   C. *Cinnamon Town*
   D. *Apache Sunrise*

TIP 7: When reading information passages, form your own opinions about what you are reading. Find details in the passage to support your opinion.

As you learned in the beginning of this lesson, a statement of fact can be checked. An opinion is a statement that cannot be checked. An opinion is what someone thinks. When you are reading an information passage, it is a good idea to form your own opinion about what the author is saying. Decide if you agree or disagree with the author. Look for reasons in the passage to support your opinion.

Read the following letter to an editor and answer Numbers 11 and 12.

> Dear Editor,
> I am writing this letter to explain why the mayor is wrong in her decision to cut down the old oak tree on Main Street. As you know, the mayor wants to cut down this tree to make room for a parking lot. She thinks that the city needs more parking spaces. She thinks that if people have room to park their cars, more people will shop there. The old oak tree is over 100 years old! It is beautiful. A parking lot is ugly. Cutting down the oak tree is a terrible idea. It is much more important than a parking lot.
> Sincerely,
> Ramona Diaz

11. Do you think it is a good idea to cut down the old oak tree to make room for a parking lot?

____

____

____

____

____

12. Give two reasons to support your answer.

1. ____

____

____

2. ____

____

____

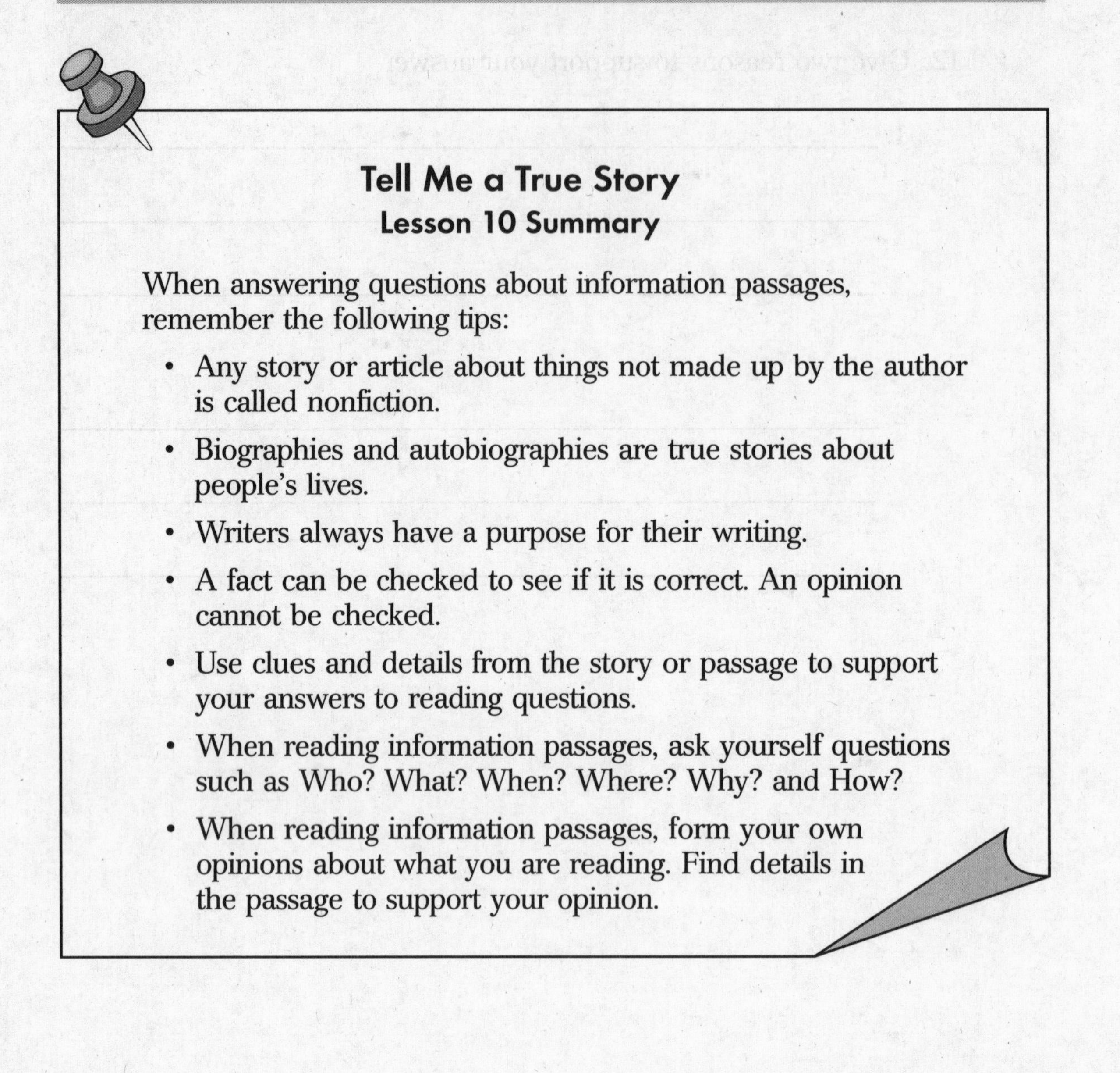

Tell Me a True Story

Lesson 10 Summary

When answering questions about information passages, remember the following tips:

- Any story or article about things not made up by the author is called nonfiction.
- Biographies and autobiographies are true stories about people's lives.
- Writers always have a purpose for their writing.
- A fact can be checked to see if it is correct. An opinion cannot be checked.
- Use clues and details from the story or passage to support your answers to reading questions.
- When reading information passages, ask yourself questions such as Who? What? When? Where? Why? and How?
- When reading information passages, form your own opinions about what you are reading. Find details in the passage to support your opinion.

CRCT Practice

Directions: Read the passage, then answer the questions.

Clara Barton—Angel of Mercy

by Rick Zollo

When Clara Barton was growing up, she wanted to help people. Her first job was as a teacher. For 18 years, she taught school in Massachusetts and New Jersey.

In 1861, the United States was torn apart by the Civil War. Clara knew she wanted to help the Union Army, so she went to Washington, D.C. At first, Clara carried supplies to the soldiers. Then she began to help care for the wounded men. She did such a fine job that soon she was put in charge of the other nurses.

After the war, Clara helped search for soldiers who were missing in battle. She also helped their families. So much work and worry made Clara very tired. She went to Europe for a long rest.

In Switzerland, Clara met other people who helped soldiers and their families. They belonged to a group called the International Red Cross. When Clara Barton returned to the United States, she helped start another group of caring people called the American Red Cross.

Clara knew that people need help even in peacetime. The American Red Cross helped out when there were floods, hurricanes, tornadoes, or other disasters. Clara Barton was the leader of the American Red Cross for more than 20 years.

Clara showed that one person who cared about helping people could really make a big difference.

Sample True Story Questions

1. When Clara Barton FIRST went to help the Union Army, what did she do?

A. carried supplies

B. directed other nurses

C. cared for the wounded

D. searched for missing soldiers

2. This passage is an example of

A. a newspaper article.

B. an autobiography.

C. an editorial.

D. a biography.

3. The author of this passage would MOST LIKELY describe Clara Barton as

A. caring.

B. sad.

C. tired.

D. funny.

4. What is the author's purpose in this passage?

A. to convince readers to do something

B. to tell about someone important

C. to give information about an event

D. to argue against an idea

5. Which sentence from the passage is an opinion?

A. At first, Clara carried supplies to the soldiers.

B. After the war, Clara helped search for soldiers who were missing in battle.

C. Clara Barton was the leader of the American Red Cross for more than 20 years.

D. Clara showed that one person who cared about helping people could really make a big difference.

Additional Practice Questions

6. Why did Clara Barton go to Europe?

A. Her friends lived in Europe.

B. A war was going on in Europe.

C. She had to visit the Red Cross in Switzerland.

D. She was tired and wanted to visit Europe to rest.

"The American Red Cross helped out when there were floods, hurricanes, tornadoes, or other <u>disasters</u>."

7. Which of the following means the same as *disasters*?

A. great enemies

B. all-time favorites

C. money rewards

D. terrible accidents

Lesson 11

Stories for the Stage

In Lesson 9, you learned about the different types of writing. You learned that fiction writers make up a time, a place, a group of characters, and a story. You learned that there are many different types of fiction. Adventure stories, mysteries, folktales, and poetry are types of fiction. In this lesson, you will learn about another kind of fiction: plays.

Plays (sometime called **dramas**) are stories written to be performed by actors on a stage in front of a live audience or in front of a television or movie camera. The author of a play is called a **playwright**. Because they are meant to be read aloud, plays are written differently than other made-up stories. Like other stories, however, plays have characters, settings, and plots.

In this lesson, you will learn about plays and how they are different from other kinds of stories.

TIP 1: Plays are divided into acts and scenes.

Just as long stories are divided into sections and chapters, plays are divided into parts called **acts** and **scenes.** Acts are the largest parts of a play. Usually, an act has two or more scenes. Each scene has a **setting.** A setting is where the play takes place. The beginning of a play might look like this:

Act I

Scene I

(SETTING: Two students seated in the front of classroom, listening to a teacher speak.)

Now answer Number 1 to make sure you understand what you have read.

1. Which of these statements is the MOST correct?

   A. Acts are divided into scenes.

   B. Scenes are divided into acts.

   C. Plays are divided into acts only.

   D. Plays are divided into scenes only.

TIP 2: Plays do not use as much description as fictional stories.

Most fiction tells you how the characters look and act. This is called **description.** Plays do not need a lot of description because they take place in front of the audience's eyes. The people in the audience can see how the characters look, dress, and act. They can also see what the setting (or **scenery**) looks like.

In a play, the writer gives only a little bit of information about what the setting–the stage–should look like. This lets the people putting on the play know what the scenery should look like. These items of information are called **stage directions.** Stage directions are given at the beginning of each act and scene. They are enclosed in parentheses. Read the stage directions below.

Act I
Scene 2

(Slowly the lights come up and Nora appears, walking into the kitchen wearing a bathrobe.)

2. Why do plays contain less description than fictional stories?

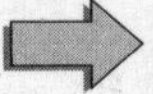

TIP 3: Actors and the characters they play are known as the cast.

Authors list the **cast** of characters at the beginning of the play. The cast is usually listed in one of three ways:

- in the order that characters first appear in the play.
- from most important character to least important character.
- with character roles in alphabetical order.

Read the "cast of characters" below.

CAST OF CHARACTERS:
NORA, a dressmaker
SID, her older son
FRANK, her younger son
CLARE, a neighbor
BEN, Sid's best friend

3. Who is Nora's neighbor?
   A. Sid
   B. Frank
   C. Clare
   D. Ben

TIP 4: The spoken words of a play are called dialogue.

The **dialogue** of a play is very important. Dialogue refers to the words that the characters speak. It tells the audience what the characters feel and think. Playwrights can't use their own voice to explain things, the way that story writers often do. Read the dialogue below.

NORA: Sid, is Frank with you?

SID: No, Mom. Sid went to see Clare.

NORA: You didn't let him go alone, did you?

SID: No, of course I didn't. Ben went with him. They'll be back any minute now.

4. In a play, each character's spoken words are called
   A. actions.
   B. dialogue.
   C. setting.
   D. music.

Drama Words

Act – a part of a play (Each act is usually made up of smaller parts called scenes.)

Cast – the characters in a play, and the actors who play those characters

Dialogue – the spoken words of a play

Playwright – the author of a play

Scene – part of a play's act

Set – the stage and scenery used in a play

Setting – the place, time, and location where the action takes place

Stage – a platform upon which actors move and speak

Stage directions – instructions that tell the actors where and how to move

Theatre – a building with a stage and seats for the audience

TIP 5: Stage directions tell the actors how and where to move on the stage.

Playwrights use stage direction to tell the actors how and where to move. These directions are usually placed inside parentheses ( ) and printed in *italic* type. Read these lines from a play.

NORA: (*calling*) Frank! You come here right now!

FRANK: (*entering the kitchen*) Hi, Mom. What's wrong with you?

NORA: (*shaking her head*) What's wrong with me? You've been gone over an hour. And where is Ben?

5. Which is a stage direction?
   A. NORA:
   B. What's wrong with you?
   C. Frank!
   D. (*calling*)

Lights, Camera, Action!

Dialogue shows actors what to say, but it also gives clues about how they might say it. Sometimes you can tell how a character will sound just by reading his or her lines. For example, if a character named Mrs. Jones has a line that reads, "Get off my lawn this minute!" you can probably guess that Mrs. Jones wouldn't speak in a very polite voice.

Practice saying the following lines out loud. Be sure to say each line in a way you think fits with that character. If you think a character would sound angry, for example, you could scrunch up your face and speak in a sharp voice.

MARCI: May I please have another apple, kind sir?

MR. JENKINS: Hey you! Watch where you're going!

SAM: My dog Jasper is the cutest puppy in the world.

DONALD: I've asked you a thousand times, and I'll ask you again. Are you ever going to clean up your room?

Stories for the Stage
Lesson 11 Summary

When answering questions about plays, remember the following tips:

- Plays are divided into acts and scenes.
- Plays do not use as much description as fictional stories.
- Actors and the characters they play are known as the cast.
- The spoken words of a play are called dialogue (DYE-uh-log).
- Stage directions tell the actors how and where to move on the stage.

CRCT Practice

Directions: Read the play, and then answer the questions.

The Elves and the Shoemaker

by Jakob and Wilhelm Grimm

adapted for the stage by Mike Acton

CAST OF CHARACTERS:
FRANZ, *a shoemaker*
MAMA, *his wife*
TEENY, *an elf*
TINY, *an assistant elf*
MAN, *a customer*

Act I
Scene 1

(SETTING: The workshop of Franz, a poor shoemaker. There is a bare window at the rear of the stage. On the left side of the stage is an open closet door and a door to the living area. On the right side is an entry door with a signal bell. A shoemaker's workbench with a three-legged stool is near the center of the stage. A rocking chair sits near the living-area door. It is night. A candle burns on the workbench. Franz sits on his stool, using a large pair of scissors to cut leather for a pair of shoes. He peers over his glasses and speaks to his wife, who is rocking slowly.)

FRANZ: Mama, this is the last of our leather. I will finish cutting it tonight and make a pair of shoes in the morning. If I can sell those shoes, we can buy food.

MAMA: But Franz, what are we going to do tonight? We have nothing but a few cups of flour, and that (*Pointing to the workbench*) is our last candle.

FRANZ: I know, Mama. We'll have to go to bed hungry tonight, and hope that I can sell a pair of shoes tomorrow. (*Picks up the candle and walks toward the rocking chair*) Come along, Mama. Let's sleep now.

(*The couple moves slowly through the living-area door. Stage lights dim, then go off. The candle flickers in the living area for a few seconds, then goes out. Darkness.*)

Act I
Scene 2

(*Slowly the lights come up and Franz appears in a nightgown and nightcap, holding a burning candle. He approaches the workbench in bare feet, yawning.*)

FRANZ: (*Stares at a completed pair of shoes sitting on the workbench*) What is this? What is this thing I am seeing? (*Picks up each shoe, one at a time, and examines them closely*) Such beautiful stitches. Masterful! This is the work of a skilled cobbler![1] Wonderful work! (*Loudly*) Mama! Mama! Come here. Come look what I've found!

MAMA: (*Rushing toward the workbench in nightgown and kerchief*) What is it, Franz? You'll wake the whole neighborhood. What have you found?

FRANZ: Look, Mama. These shoes. Somebody has finished them for me. And Mama, it's the work of a master cobbler. Look, see for yourself.

MAMA: They are very nice, Papa. But now we need to sell them.

(*The entrance door opens, its bell rings, and a well-dressed customer enters.*)

MAN: Good morning, shoemaker. Still in your nightclothes, I see. Strange bunch, you cobblers! (*Franz pulls off his nightcap and bows.*) Oh well! Let's get on with it. I need a pair of shoes in a hurry.

MAMA: (*Sitting in her rocking chair*) Franz makes the finest pair of shoes in all the Black Forest.

[1] **cobbler:** person who works with leather.

FRANZ: Why, thank you, Mama. Please excuse my nightclothes, sir. I have not had time to dress. If your worship pleases, I have just finished this pair. (*Hands the shoes to the customer*) Try them on. Here, have my seat.

MAN: (*Seating himself on Franz's stool and trying on the shoes*) Why shoemaker, these are perfect. What care you have taken in putting this pair together. I'll buy them. What is the cost?

FRANZ: Four marks,[2] sir.

MAN: Here, my good man, take eight marks. This is a fine pair of shoes, certainly worth more than four marks. Thank you. I shall return to order more shoes from you in the future. Good-bye.

FRANZ: Thank you, sir. Good day. (*Customer exits*) Mama, Mama, we have enough money to buy food and leather for at least two pair of shoes. We owe our success to an unknown master shoemaker and a generous customer. (*They hug each other in happiness.*)

(*Curtain*)

[2] **marks:** old German coins, today worth about fifty cents.

Act II

Scene 1

(*SETTING: Two weeks later. Franz and Mama are dressed in much better clothing. The room has several burning candles. Curtains have been placed on the window. Additional furniture is located around the stage. Franz is at his workbench cutting leather and Mama is in her rocking chair.*)

MAMA: Twenty pair of shoes you sold today. If tomorrow's shoes sell as fast as today's, we will soon be very rich.

FRANZ: (*Cutting the last of the leather for tomorrow's shoes*) Yes, Mama. Life has been very good to us. But I want to find out who is helping us. Let's hide in the closet tonight and see if we can see our helpful friend.

MAMA: (*Rising*) That's a great idea, Papa. We can hide behind the coats in the closet. Will you leave a candle burning?

FRANZ: I never have before, Mama.

(*Both characters rise and put out the candles as the stage lights dim. After Franz and Mama are safely in the closet, the stage lights go out. Shortly, a clock strikes midnight, the entrance door opens slowly, and Teeny and Tiny enter on tiptoe followed by a blue spotlight. They are barefoot, bearded, and dressed in rags. Slowly the lights come up and the spotlight fades.*)

TEENY: Tiny, you sew the uppers and be careful with the tongue.

TINY: Be careful with the tongue? I haven't said a thing, Teeny.

TEENY: Just get to work.

TINY: Yes, sir.

(*Both elves begin to work at great speed, sewing, tacking, and gluing. When they finish, they line the shoes along the edge of the workbench, shake hands, and tiptoe out the entrance door. Stage lights dim. Franz and Mama come out of the coat closet and light a candle on the workbench.*)

FRANZ: What strange little men. Mama, I think we should show our thanks by making them new clothes and shoes. What do you think?

MAMA: Oh, Papa. I think that would be ever so nice. I'll sew the clothes if you make the shoes. Let's sleep now and tomorrow we will begin.

(*The couple exits slowly through the living-area door. Stage lights dim, then go black. The candle flickers in the living area for a few seconds, then goes out. Darkness.*)

Act II
Scene 2

(*SETTING: Late the following evening. Stage lights brighten. Franz and Mama admire the new clothes and shoes they have made for the elves.*)

FRANZ: It's almost midnight, Mama. Let's hide again and see what happens when the elves find their new clothes.

(*Franz and Mama again hide in the closet. Stage lights dim. A clock strikes twelve. Teeny and Tiny tiptoe through the door and head straight for the workbench. They are followed by a blue spotlight.*)

TINY: Look, boss. New clothes! Now we can party with the rest of the elves.

TEENY: And new shoes. Isn't it wonderful? It makes me want to sing.

TINY: Oh, no. (*Holding his ears*) Surely it isn't that wonderful, is it?

TEENY: (*Singing*)
Oh, happy little elves are we
Who get new clothes and shoes for free.
With brand new jackets and new pants
We'll join the elves in song and dance.

We'll work no more for Cobbler Franz.
We'll party in new caps and pants.
For weeks we've helped our friend make shoes,
And now we'll do just as we choose.

(*The elves skip through the door and into the night. Spotlight off. Stage lights remain dim. Franz and Mama come out of the coat closet and light a candle. Stage lights come up.*)

MAMA: Have they left us forever, Papa?

FRANZ: Yes, Mama, they have gone. But not before they helped us build a fine business. We will be hungry no more. Let us go to bed now, Mama, and dream sweet dreams.

(*Taking the candle, the two exit to the living area. The lights lower from dim to darkness. Again, the candle flickers from the living area for a few seconds and goes out.*)

(*Curtain*)

Sample Drama Questions

1. This passage is an example of

A. a poem.

B. a story.

C. drama.

D. nonfiction.

2. Which part of the passage shows that it is make-believe?

A. A shoemaker makes shoes.

B. A customer buys shoes.

C. Two elves make shoes.

D. A couple goes to bed hungry.

3. What problem does the shoemaker have in the beginning of the passage?

A. He needs to find some elves.

B. He needs better tools.

C. He needs food and candles.

D. He needs to buy a new rocking chair.

4. Where does this passage take place?

A. in a bedroom

B. in a workshop

C. in a living-area

D. in a basement

5. This passage is MAINLY about a couple who

A. make shoes at night.

B. get help from elves.

C. sell items of clothing.

D. need candles and food.

Additional Practice Questions

6. Both Teeny and Tiny are

A. small.

B. bossy.

C. young.

D. brave.

7. How do you think the couple feels at the end of the passage?

A. hungry

B. foolish

C. worried

D. pleased

8. How much does the customer pay Franz for the first pair of shoes he sells?

A. 2 marks

B. 4 marks

C. 6 marks

D. 8 marks

9. In "The Elves and the Shoemaker," which of these happens LAST?

A. Franz and Mama hide to find out who is making the shoes.

B. The elves sing and skip through the door and out into the night.

C. A customer buys a pair of shoes.

D. Mama says, "That is our last candle."

Lesson 12

Words That Sing

A poem is a special kind of writing. It can be about made-up people and places, or it can be about something that really happened. Because each and every word in a poem is so important, you usually have to read a poem more slowly than you would other kinds of writing.

As you read the following poem, think about how poems are different from other stories you've read in this book.

Mother Says It's Time to Sleep

by Juanita Kopaska

It's shameful that I'm off to bed
When skies are blue and sun is red,
But Mother says it's time to sleep.
I wish she'd tell my mind and feet!

Although my eyes are getting tired,
My mind and feet are both on fire!
I want to climb the pasture gate
And watch the brown cows as they wait

For Dad to milk them in the barn.
But now it's up to bed. Gosh darn!
My eyes hum softly, "Time to dream–"
While feet and mind say, "Run!" and "Scream!"

But Mother says it's time to sleep.
She doesn't want to hear a peep.
And so it's into bed I climb,
Although it's just past suppertime.

Poems Paint Pictures in Our Minds

In some ways, poems are like most other kinds of writing. They can tell a story. They can paint beautiful pictures in our minds. They can be serious, or they can be funny. And they can make us feel happy or sad.

TIP 1: Look for the poem's main idea.

When you first read a poem, you may not understand every word or every line. Don't worry. After you read it the first time, just ask yourself, "What is this mainly about?"

Once you know the writer's main idea, you can read the poem again to help you get the meaning of each line. Rereading the poem will help you understand it better. It will also help you see the special ways that poets put words together.

Read the poem "Mother Says It's Time to Sleep" all the way through—again. Read carefully to find out what this poem is mainly about.

1. What is the main idea of "Mother Says It's Time to Sleep"?

____

____

____

____

TIP 2: Listen for words that have the same end sound (rhyme).

Rhyming words have the same end sound. Here are some examples of rhyming words.

blue / shoe	hat / cat
man / can	my / pie
sea / be	could / wood

Notice that the endings of the words don't have to be spelled the same way, but they must make the same sound.

Here is another short poem. As you read it, watch for rhyming words.

Marvin Made a Model Ship

by Dexter Evans

Marvin made a model ship
Of playing cards and glue.
It was a graceful sailing ship
When Marvin was all through.

But, getting up one early morn,
He found his ship a wreck.
His brother Johnny smashed it flat
When Dad called, "Hit the deck!"

2. Which word from the poem rhymes with the word *glue*?
   A. ship
   B. morn
   C. wreck
   D. through

3. Which word from the poem rhymes with the word *wreck*?
   A. deck
   B. ship
   C. glue
   D. flat

TIP 3: Writers sometimes break poems into stanzas (groupings of lines).

Just as most writing is broken into paragraphs, many poems are broken into groups of lines called **stanzas.**

Read the following poem, then answer Number 4.

Barry and Larry

by Mickey Toom

Barry liked hiking
And Larry liked biking
And both liked to go to the zoo.
When Larry had candy,
Then Barry had candy.
What was one's, was the other one's, too.

When Barry caught mumps,
Larry got the same lumps,
And each had the face of a clown.
So Larry gave Barry
A gift to help carry
Him through till the swelling went down.

Larry liked airplanes
And Barry liked old trains.
Together, they liked playing ball,
But it ended when Larry
Saw his best friend Barry
Hold hands with a girl at the mall!

4. How many stanzas does the poem "Barry and Larry" have?
   A. 1
   B. 2
   C. 3
   D. 4

TIP 4: Idioms say one thing but mean something else.

It's raining cats and dogs.

Billy is so hungry he could eat a horse.

Shandra cried her eyes out.

These phrases are **idioms**. The first one doesn't mean that kittens and cocker spaniels are actually falling out of the sky. It simply means that it is raining very hard. In the second one, Billy isn't really planning to eat a horse. The idiom just means that he is very hungry. And Shandra didn't really wash her eyes away. The idiom simply means she cried a lot.

5. Draw a line from the idioms on the left to their real meanings on the right.

walking on air	stop talking
neat as a pin	everything in its place
hold your tongue	wait a minute
get wind of it	help me
lend me a hand	very happy
keep your shirt on	hear about it

TIP 5: Writers compare things by using similes (saying one thing is like or as another).

Writers often try to help us see everyday things in new ways. One way they do this is by using one thing to make us think of another thing. When they say one thing is like or as another, they are using a **simile**.

For example, a writer might say that *a red ball is like an apple* or that *a ball is as red as an apple.* Most people don't think of red balls when they take a bite out of an apple. And they don't usually think of an apple when they bounce a red ball. But comparing an apple to a red ball helps us see how the two things are alike.

6. Finish the following sentence by comparing a soft bed to something else. You'll be using a simile.

   This bed is as soft as ______________________________.

7. Now write your own sentence comparing one thing to another using a simile.

   ____

   ____

   ____

   ____

Why would a writer go to the trouble of making up comparisons? Because these comparisons make poems and stories more fun to read. They help us to imagine the world in new ways.

Do you know these lines by Ann and Jane Taylor?

from

The Star

Twinkle, twinkle, little star
How I wonder what you are!
Up above the world so high,
Like a diamond in the sky.

8. The writers compare a little star to
   A. a child.
   B. the sky.
   C. the world.
   D. a diamond.

TIP 6: Writers also compare things by using metaphors (saying one thing really is another thing).

Sometimes, the writer says that one thing really is another. This kind of writing is called a **metaphor** (MET-uh-for). In the following poem, the **speaker** (narrator) describes his bicycle using a metaphor.

My Rocket Ship

by Michael Roberts

I have a little rocket ship
With shiny spokes and chrome–
And ten speeds I can change at will
When I blast off for home.

I wear my helmet fastened tight
And lean into the wind–
When we are streaking through the stars
Or up the driveway's bend.

The speaker does not say that his bike is like a rocket ship. He uses a metaphor and says that the bike is a rocket ship.

9. Circle at least three words or phrases from the poem that could be used to describe both a rocket and a bicycle.

10. In the box that follows, draw a picture about the poem.

Imagine that you are lying on your back and looking up into the afternoon sky as you read the next poem. Then answer the questions that follow.

Clouds

by Christina G. Rossetti

White sheep, white sheep,
On a blue hill,
When the wind stops
You all stand still.

When the wind blows
You walk away slow.
White sheep, white sheep,
Where do you go?

11. The author writes about "white sheep." What is she describing?
    A. trees
    B. kites
    C. clouds
    D. sheep

12. What is the "blue hill"?
    A. the sky
    B. a flower
    C. a meadow
    D. a mountain

13. What does the author mean when she says, "You walk away slow"?
    A. The sun is crossing the sky.
    B. The sheep are looking for grass.
    C. Clouds are moving across the sky.
    D. Flowers are blowing in the wind.

TIP 7: Sensory words are words that excite our senses of sight, hearing, touch, taste, and smell.

The word *sensory* has to do with our senses. **Sensory words** help us to see, hear, feel, smell, or taste what the author is writing about. Here are some examples of sensory words doing their job to help you better understand what the author is talking about.

Sight – Dew sparkled in the grass like a million tiny diamonds.

Hearing – The airplane thundered from the runway and roared into the night sky.

Touch – The kitten's tongue felt like warm sandpaper as it licked the milk from my finger.

Taste – Uncle Ned's homemade chili slid down my throat like a burning cactus.

Smell – Mom's pie filled the air with smells of cinnamon, apples, and freshly baked crust.

14. Write a sentence using sensory words that tells about how something looks (sight).

____

____

____

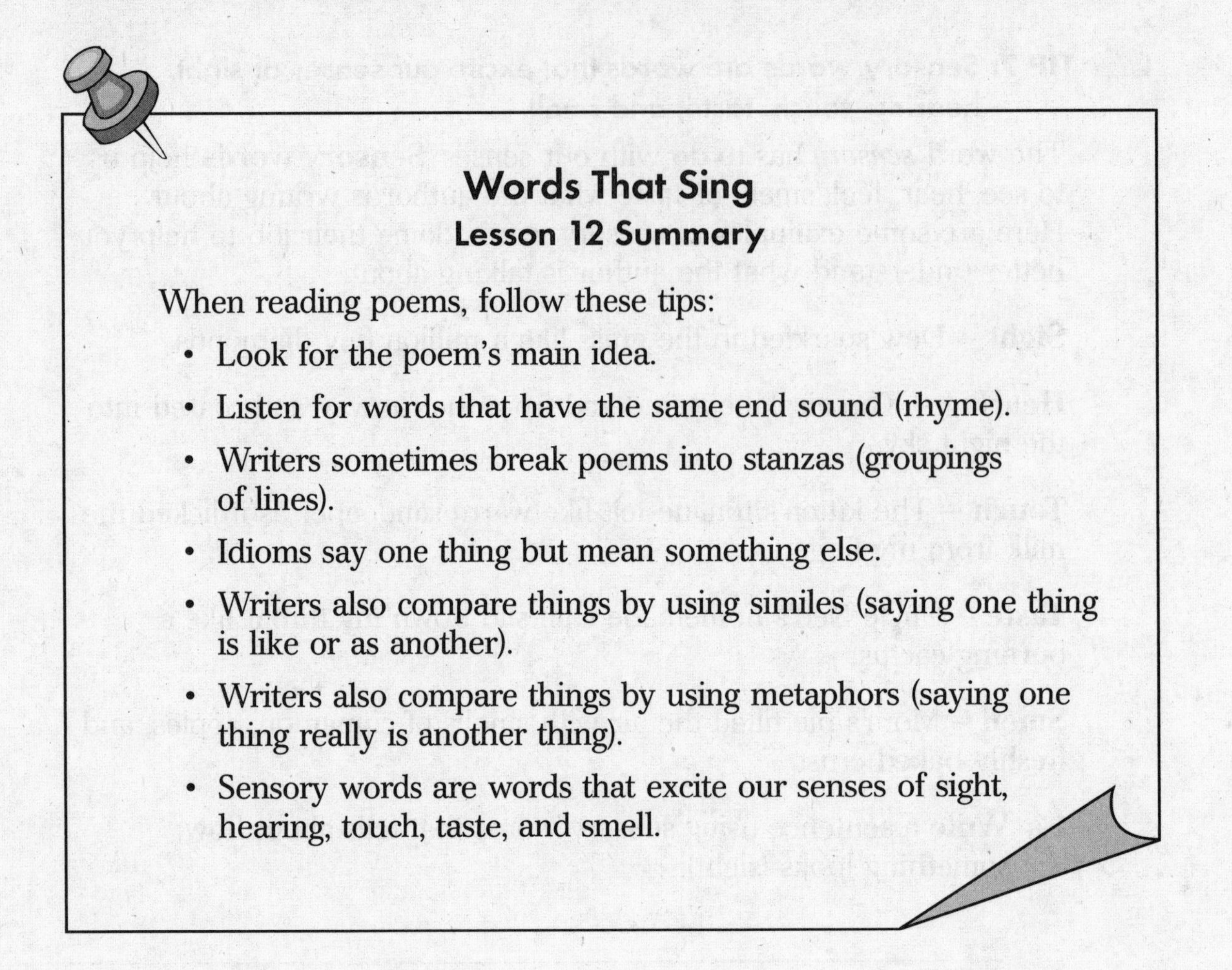

Words That Sing

Lesson 12 Summary

When reading poems, follow these tips:

- Look for the poem's main idea.
- Listen for words that have the same end sound (rhyme).
- Writers sometimes break poems into stanzas (groupings of lines).
- Idioms say one thing but mean something else.
- Writers also compare things by using similes (saying one thing is like or as another).
- Writers also compare things by using metaphors (saying one thing really is another thing).
- Sensory words are words that excite our senses of sight, hearing, touch, taste, and smell.

CRCT Practice

Directions: Read the poem, then answer the questions.

Toy Talk

by Tiffany Carlisle

Each night the toys inside their box
Lie still, except for moonlight talks.
One winter night the red drum said,
"The world's so loud it hurts my head."

"No, no," the windup monkey's voice
Insisted as he told the toys,
"Let's talk about the world I've found.
It backflips every time I'm wound!"

The top was silent, then she said,
"The world spins round and round my head.
Sometimes it gets in such a tizzy
My face turns green and I get dizzy."

"No. None of you is right," the ball
Said certainly to one and all.
"The world goes up when I go down,
And bounces like a circus clown."

The hobbyhorse across the room
Moved gently in the dust and gloom.
He'd watched the edges of the earth
And knew the world rocked back and forth.

Sample Poetry Questions

1. How many stanzas does this poem have?

A. 3

B. 4

C. 5

D. 6

2. What is this poem MOSTLY about?

A. toys that talk to each other only at night

B. toys that think the world spins very fast

C. toys that think the world goes up and down

D. toys that don't really understand the world at all

3. Which toy does not speak out loud?

A. the top

B. the ball

C. the hobbyhorse

D. the windup monkey

4. In the first stanza, which word rhymes with head?

A. box

B. talks

C. hurts

D. said

5. What kind of rhyme pattern does the poem have?

A. Every other line rhymes.

B. Every pair of lines rhyme.

C. The second and fourth lines rhyme.

D. The second and third lines rhyme.

Additional Practice Questions

6. The author MOST LIKELY wrote this poem to

A. entertain the reader.

B. prove that toys can talk.

C. teach the reader about drums.

D. persuade the reader to buy a toy.

"'No, no,' the windup monkey's voice
Insisted as he told the toys"

7. The word *insisted* means

A. lied.

B. sang.

C. whistled.

D. demanded.

8. If the poet added a verse about in-line skates, it would probably say which of the following?

A. The world speeds past under me.

B. The world bounces from side to side.

C. The drum is right, the world is too loud.

D. I can't see the world from inside this toy box.

Lesson 13

Comparing Stories

"Hey, Mia, have you ever read *The Secret Garden?*"

"No, Ginger, I haven't. But I saw the movie on television."

"Yeah. I saw that movie, too. The book had a lot more detail. Do you want to borrow my copy?"

"Great idea, Ginger! I'll come by your house tonight and pick it up."

"See you, then."

The same story can be told in many different ways. By choosing what to put in the movie and what to leave out, the director of *The Secret Garden* could have told the story in a very different way than its author, Frances Hodgson Burnett. The same thing is true of fictional stories that tell about the same events.

Read these two stories based on the fairy tale "Snow White and the Seven Dwarfs." The first story is told by Snow White. The second one is told by the evil queen's magic mirror.

Story 1

Snow White

an adapted fairy tale

The last three days of my life have been difficult, and it all started with the evil queen. Her magic mirror told her that *I* am the "fairest in the land." This made her very angry. So she told a hunter to take me out into the woods and leave me there. He was supposed to take me so far away that I would never find my way back. But he is a good man and did not want to do this. He felt bad for me and left me in the nearby woods instead, where I would be able to easily find my way back home. Now, the queen thinks that I am gone and that she is the most beautiful woman in the kingdom.

As I was trying to find my way out of the woods, it grew dark and cold. I was afraid until I noticed a light in the distance. I followed the light and discovered that it came from a small cottage. No one answered the door when I knocked. It was too cold to sit outside, so I stepped into the cottage and waited in front of the fire for a while. Then I climbed into one of seven little beds.

Before long, I heard voices. I quickly pulled the covers over my head. The voices belonged to seven dwarfs! When the little men found me, they were happy to meet me! They were very nice and listened to my story. They said I could live with them if I wanted to. I'm happy and safe here. Now I will never have to see the queen again!

Story 2

The Magic Mirror's Letter to the Evil Queen

an adapted fairy tale

Dear Evil Queen:

As you know, I've been trapped in this story with you for more than 500 years. I have grown sick and tired of the same old question every single day: "Mirror, mirror, on the wall, who's the fairest of them all?" Why couldn't you ask me something new? You could ask, "Why do the people in my kingdom think I'm so awful?" or, "Does this dress make me look evil?" There are so many questions you really should be asking! Do you not care about the happiness of your people?

The most important thing I must tell you is the truth. Here is the real answer to your question: Snow White is the fairest of them all. The people love her because she is not only beautiful, but kind and caring, too. You should not hate Snow White for being a good and lovely person! Your anger has made you less fair. But Snow White's goodness has made her more fair.

Oh, all the nights I have had to listen to your evil plans to get rid of Snow White! Your anger puts us all in danger. So I quit! I am leaving the castle, never to return! I'm off to see the world! Good-bye, Evil Queen!

Sincerely,

Your Former Magic Mirror

TIP 1: Find out who is telling each story.

It's important to know who is telling the story. This is called the story's **point of view.** If you and a friend (or any two people) tell the same story, each will tell it differently. What may be important to you may not be important to your friend, so you will include different details. While you might think something is funny, your friend might not think so. And while you might think someone is nice, your friend might think that the person is rude. Think back to the two stories you just read about Snow White and answer the following questions.

1. Who is telling the story in Story 1?
   A. the magic mirror
   B. Snow White
   C. the queen
   D. a hunter

2. Who is telling the story in Story 2?
   A. the magic mirror
   B. Snow White
   C. the queen
   D. a hunter

TIP 2: Compare the details in both stories.

When you're asked to compare two stories, first see whether they both give some of the same details. The two stories you just read tell about Snow White and her evil stepmother. But each story gives different details.

3. Which detail is in BOTH stories?
   A. The queen finds out that Snow White is "the fairest of them all."
   B. It becomes dark and cold.
   C. Snow White is living in a nearby wood.
   D. Snow White meets the seven dwarfs.

4. Which detail is given only in Story 1?
   A. The magic mirror leaves the queen.
   B. The magic mirror is upset with the queen.
   C. The queen talks to her magic mirror.
   D. Snow White discovers a light coming from a small cottage.

TIP 3: Compare what the characters say and do.

A fiction writer sets the tone of a story through what its characters say and do. Try to find out what the writer thinks about each character by comparing them.

5. In Story 1, the hunter is like Snow White because he is
   A. lost.
   B. kind.
   C. afraid.
   D. foolish.

6. Snow White is different from the evil queen because she is
   A. unhappy.
   B. angry.
   C. well liked.
   D. tricky.

TIP 4: Look for ways in which one story adds to your understanding of another.

Sometimes the information given in one story will provide you with a deeper understanding of a second story. Notice how Story 1 gives you a better feeling for Snow White's problems and concerns, and Story 2 gives you a better feeling for the magic mirror and the queen's problems and concerns.

7. How does Story 2 help you better understand the evil queen's actions in Story 1?
   A. It tells that the hunter knows the queen is evil.
   B. It tells why the queen does not like Snow White.
   C. It tells that the queen has a magic mirror.
   D. It tells why Snow White decides to live with the dwarfs.

8. What does the reader learn about Snow White in Story 2?
   A. The people in the kingdom love her.
   B. She should be afraid of the hunter.
   C. The dwarfs offer to take care of her.
   D. She will soon return to the village.

TIP 5: Compare the plots of each story.

The **plot** of a story is that story's actions, what actually happens. Seeing how the plot of one story is similar to another can give you a better understanding of both stories. The plots of the stories you have just read are similar in some ways. Try to decide what is the same or similar about these two stories.

9. What main event is told about in both stories?

____

____

____

____

TIP 6: Compare the settings of each story.

The **setting** of a story is the time and place in which the events of the story happen. Thinking about a story's setting can help you picture the story as the events unfold.

10. Where does Story 1 take place?
    A. in the queen's castle
    B. in a nearby woods
    C. in a hunter's cottage
    D. in a small village

11. Where does Story 2 take place?
    A. in the queen's castle
    B. in a nearby woods
    C. in a hunter's cottage
    D. in the dwarfs' cottage

Comparing Stories
Lesson 13 Summary

When answering questions about different selections, remember the following tips:

- Find out who is telling each story.
- Compare the details in both stories.
- Compare what the characters say and do.
- Look for ways in which one story adds to your understanding of another.
- Compare the plots of each story.
- Compare the settings of each story.

CRCT Practice

Directions: Read the stories, and then answer the questions.

Story 1

Turkey Girl

a folktale of the Zuni Indians retold by Red Gomez

Turkey Girl lived in a farming village with two mean stepsisters. They were called Yellow Corn and Blue Corn. They made Turkey Girl do all the chores. She even had to take care of all the village turkeys.

Now, every year there was a festival called the Corn Dance. Turkey Girl wanted to go to the Corn Dance, but her stepsisters would not let her. "What would you wear?" they asked. "You have only rags for clothes. Stay with your friends, the turkeys. We will go to the dance instead and dance with the bravest warriors."

Poor Turkey Girl was sad. She took her flock of turkeys out to a patch of wild grain and sang them the saddest songs.

They took pity on poor Turkey Girl. "We will make clothes for you to go to the dance," they said. So, they made Turkey Girl a beautiful robe, soft moccasins, and a belt of feathers. "Go to the dance, but be back by sundown to take us to shelter," the turkeys said. "That's when the coyotes come out looking for dinner."

Turkey Girl went to the Corn Dance and was so happy. The bravest warriors waited in line to dance with her. Turkey Girl was so proud. She could see that her stepsisters were angry and jealous.

The hour came when the sun set behind the mountains. Turkey Girl was still dancing.

Suddenly Turkey Girl remembered. She hurried back to her flock. "Oh, my poor turkeys!" she screamed, "I have let you down." Then Turkey Girl began to cry.

When she returned to the patch of grain, the turkeys were gone.

"Turkey Girl has forgotten about us," they had gobbled. Then they had flown off in every direction to escape the hungry coyotes.

Turkey Girl always remembered those turkeys and never forgave herself for not returning to help them on time.

Remember this, children. Don't be like Turkey Girl! Just because you're having a good time, don't forget those who have helped you or those who depend upon you.

Story 2

Maha and the Little Red Fish

a folktale from Iraq retold by Jill Foley

Near the sea, there once lived a little girl named Maha with her father, her stepmother, and her stepsister. When her father was at home, the stepmother spoke to Maha as sweet as honey. But when he went to the sea to fish each day, the woman made Maha do all of the chores.

One day, Maha spotted a small red fish among those she was cleaning for supper. "Please return me to the sea, for I am a magic fish," said the little red fish. "I will grant you anything you wish, for kindness never goes unrewarded."

Maha removed the little fish from her net and gently returned it to the sea.

The years went by and Maha and her stepsister grew to be young women. Maha worked from sunrise to sunset, but every day she became kinder and more beautiful.

One day, the daughter of an important man was to be married. Maha wished she could go to sing and dance and watch the

bride as her hands and feet were decorated with red henna[1] stain. But instead, the stepmother made Maha help get her stepsister prepared for the celebration.

The day of the wedding, Maha went to the sea's edge to seek the advice of the little red fish. "Little fish, what should I do? Will I be my stepmother's servant forever?" asked Maha. "I wish to go to the bride's henna[2] like all of the other girls."

"You shall go," said the little red fish. "And you shall even sit next to the bride."

On the grass nearby, a silken gown, a pearl comb, and some clogs made out of gold suddenly appeared.

When Maha's stepmother and stepsister saw her at the celebration, they thought she looked very much like Maha. But then they laughed and thought how funny it would be to see Maha in such nice clothes.

All of the women at the party thought that Maha was a nice young woman. The mother of a sweet young man named Abdul saw the kindness in Maha's eyes. "You shall be the perfect bride for my son!" she exclaimed.

Soon after, Maha and Abdul were wed right near the sea, where Maha's little red fish could take part in the ceremony. Maha lived happily from that day on. She visited the little red fish nearly every day and received many more gifts from her little friend over the years.

[1]**henna:** a reddish brown dye

[2]**henna:** a party during which a bride is decorated with henna for her wedding

Sample Comparing Stories Questions

1. **Which of the following pairs of characters from both stories are MOST alike?**

   A. the coyotes and Maha's stepmother

   B. Turkey Girl's stepsisters and Maha

   C. Turkey Girl and Maha's stepsister

   D. the turkeys and the little red fish

2. **Which of the following is true about BOTH "Turkey Girl" and "Maha and the Little Red Fish"?**

   A. both are about turkeys

   B. both have happy endings

   C. both are about young women

   D. both tell about magical fish

3. **Which event in "Maha and the Little Red Fish" is like Turkey Girl going to the Corn Dance?**

   A. Maha finding a little red fish

   B. Maha cleaning fish for supper

   C. Maha going to the bride's henna

   D. Maha's stepmother acting sweet as honey

4. Which of the following happens in BOTH selections?

A. Magical animals help the main character.

B. A handsome man marries the main character.

C. A mean stepmother makes the main character work.

D. A Corn Dance makes the main character forget her duty.

5. Which event in "Turkey Girl" is MOST like the little red fish making a silken gown, pearl comb, and gold clogs appear?

A. Turkey Girl takes her flock to a patch of wild grain.

B. Brave warriors stand in line to dance with Turkey Girl.

C. Turkey Girl's stepsisters tell her she only has rags for clothes.

D. The turkeys make Turkey Girl beautiful clothes for the Corn Dance.

6. Which of the following BEST compares Maha and Turkey Girl?

A. Maha had a very happy home life. Turkey Girl had a very unhappy home life.

B. Turkey Girl had only one mean stepsister. Maha had two mean stepsisters.

C. Maha had a good time at the henna. Turkey Girl had a bad time at the Corn Dance.

D. Maha took good care of the animal that helped her. Turkey Girl forgot about the animals that helped her.

Additional Practice Questions

7. What happens to the turkeys AFTER Turkey Girl forgets about them?

A. They fly off in every direction.

B. They are eaten by hungry coyotes.

C. They hide from Turkey Girl in the wild grain.

D. They take the girl's new clothes and return her rags.

> "Maha worked from sunrise to sunset, but every day she became kinder and more beautiful."

8. The word *beautiful* means

A. full of beauty.

B. without beauty.

C. able to have beauty.

D. having the most beauty.

Lesson 14

Reading Pictures

Many times it is easier to show information using graphs, charts, or tables than it is to write page after page to explain the same thing. It is also helpful to give directions using diagrams (pictures) that show what needs to be done. This lesson will give you practice using these types of information.

TIP 1: Picture graphs show information with pictures.

Picture graphs (sometimes called pictographs) use pictures to show information. If a picture graph tells the number of ice cream cones sold each day of the week, it may use pictures of ice cream cones. For example, this picture might stand for one ice cream cone sold, or it might stand for 10 ice cream cones sold. You must look at the graph's key to find out what each picture stands for. Check out the sample key that follows:

= 5 ice cream cones

Use the picture graph that follows to answer Numbers 1 and 2.

Here is a picture graph that shows the number of boys and girls in Mrs. Smith's third-grade class. Look at the key before you answer the questions.

Boys and Girls in Mrs. Smith's Third-Grade Class

1. How many boys are in Mrs. Smith's third-grade class?
   A. two
   B. three
   C. six
   D. nine

2. How many girls are in Mrs. Smith's third-grade class?
   A. three
   B. six
   C. nine
   D. twelve

TIP 2: Circle graphs show parts of a whole.

Circle graphs are also called **pie charts** because they look like a pie that has been cut into pieces. Each slice of the pie stands for part of a whole amount. Parts of the pie can be compared by looking at the size of the pieces.

To read a circle graph you should follow these steps:

- look at the title to find out what the chart is showing
- read the label on each slice of the pie to see what it stands for

Mr. Henderson teaches 3rd Grade at an elementary school in Waynesboro, Georgia. He asked his class of 20 students to tell him the flavor of their favorite ice cream. Then he made a circle graph to show the information that he gathered. Study the pie chart that follows and answer the questions.

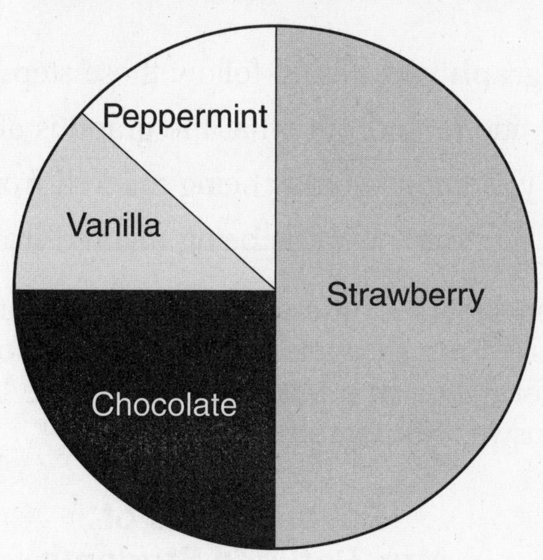

3. Which ice cream flavor was the favorite of the most students?

____

4. Which two ice cream flavors together are the favorite of about one-fourth of the students?
   A. vanilla and chocolate
   B. peppermint and vanilla
   C. vanilla and strawberry
   D. strawberry and peppermint

5. If there are 20 students in Mr. Henderson's class, how many said that strawberry was their favorite flavor?
   A. 5
   B. 10
   C. 15
   D. 20

TIP 3: Bar graphs compare different amounts of the same kinds of things.

To read a **bar graph** you should follow these steps:

- look at the title to find out what the graph is about
- make sure you know what is being marked from left to right
- make sure you know what is being marked from bottom to top

Mrs. Parker teaches 3rd Grade at an elementary school in Columbus, Georgia. She asked her students to name their favorite kind of pet. She put the information in a bar graph. Study the bar graph that follows, then answer Numbers 6 through 8.

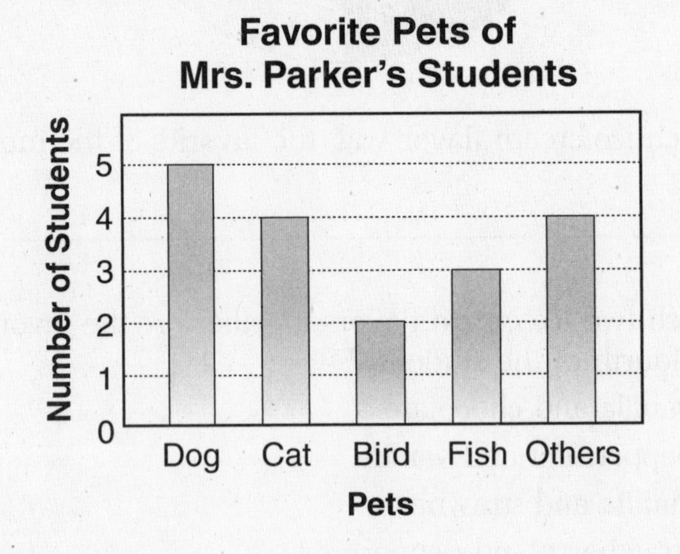

6. How many students said that dogs were their favorite pet?
   A. 2
   B. 3
   C. 4
   D. 5

7. How many students said that cats were their favorite pet?
   A. 2
   B. 3
   C. 4
   D. 5

8. If every student in the class named one favorite pet, how many children are in Mrs. Parker's class?
   A. 11
   B. 15
   C. 18
   D. 20

TIP 4: Line graphs show changes over time.

To read a **line graph** you should follow these steps:

- look at the title to find out what the graph is about
- make sure you know what is being marked from left to right
- make sure you know what is being marked from bottom to top

Billy decided to see how warm it would get during one week in his hometown of Statesboro, Georgia. He marked the high temperature every day on a line graph. Study his line graph and answer the questions that follow.

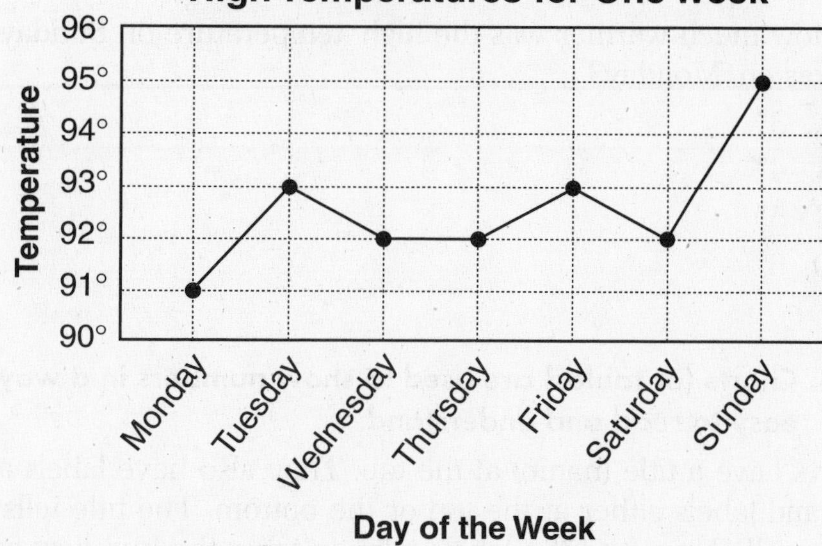

9. On which day was it the warmest?
   A. Saturday
   B. Sunday
   C. Monday
   D. Tuesday

10. On which day was the high temperature 91°?
    A. Monday
    B. Wednesday
    C. Friday
    D. Saturday

11. On which two days was the high temperature 93°?
    A. Monday and Tuesday
    B. Tuesday and Friday
    C. Wednesday and Thursday
    D. Thursday and Friday

12. How much warmer was the high temperature on Sunday than it was on Monday?
    A. 3°
    B. 4°
    C. 5°
    D. 6°

TIP 5: Charts (or tables) are used to show numbers in a way that is easy to read and understand.

Charts have a title (name) at the top. They also have labels along one side, and labels either at the top or the bottom. The title tells what the chart is all about, and the labels tell you what the numbers stand for. The boxes containing the numbers are called **cells. Rows** of cells go from left to right; **columns** of cells go from top to bottom. Look at the chart that follows. Go to the cell at Row 2, Column 3. The cell contains the number 249 and tells the reader that it is 249 miles between Augusta and Columbus.

To find the distance between two cities, find one city on the row labels and the other city on the column labels. For example, let's say you want to see how far it is from Macon to Savannah. Slide your finger along the Macon row until it comes to the Savannah column. Read the number of miles. In this case, it is 171 miles between Macon and Savannah.

To read a chart or table you should follow these steps:

- look at the title to find out what the chart is about
- make sure you know what is being labeled from left to right
- make sure you know what is being labeled from top to bottom

Miles Between Some Cities in Georgia

Column Labels / Row Labels

	Atlanta	Augusta	Columbus	Macon	Savannah
Atlanta	–	150	104	81	252
Augusta	150	–	249	124	140
Columbus	104	249	–	97	268
Macon	81	124	97	–	171
Savannah	252	140	268	171	–

13. What is the distance between Atlanta and Savannah?
    A. 150 miles
    B. 252 miles
    C. 249 miles
    D. 268 miles

14. What is the distance between Macon and Columbus?
    A. 97 miles
    B. 124 miles
    C. 171 miles
    D. 268 miles

15. What is the distance between Columbus and Augusta?
    A. 97 miles
    B. 104 miles
    C. 249 miles
    D. 268 miles

16. What is the distance between Savannah and Augusta?
    A. 81 miles
    B. 97 miles
    C. 124 miles
    D. 140 miles

17. Why is there no number shown at Row 4, Column 4?

    ____

TIP 6: Flow charts and diagrams help you see how things work, how events happen, or how parts are put together.

A **flow chart** usually tells you about how one thing causes another thing to happen. Look at this simple flow chart and answer the question that follows.

Ice melting at 70° Fahrenheit

18. According to this flow chart, what is the main cause of ice melting at 70° Fahrenheit?
    A. the passing of time
    B. the temperature going up
    C. the temperature going down
    D. the temperature staying the same

A **diagram** can tell you how to build a model airplane or how to play a new game. It can show you the parts of your new bicycle or give you a look inside a water faucet. Study this diagram of the human body, and then answer the question that follows.

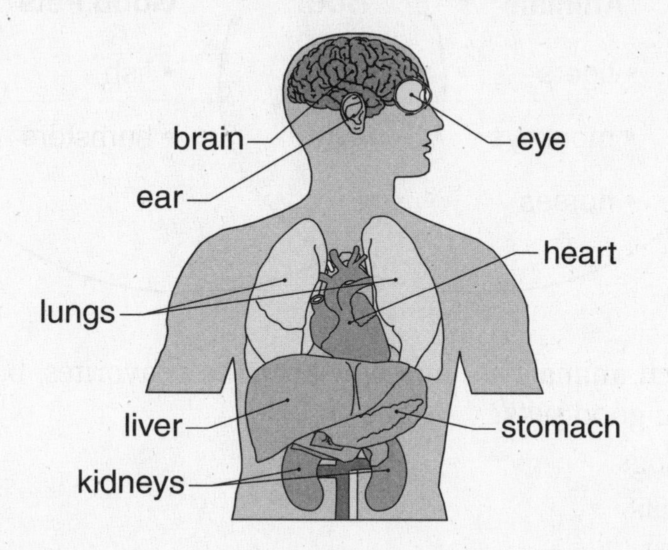

19. According to the diagram, how many lungs does a human being have?
   A. 1
   B. 2
   C. 3
   D. 4

TIP 7: Venn diagrams show you how two or more things are alike and different.

The following diagram is called a **Venn diagram**. Venn diagrams use circles or ovals to group information. The following Venn diagram shows Carmelita's picks for three things:

- her favorite animals
- animals that she thinks would make good pets
- and animals that are both her favorites and that would make good pets.

Study this Venn diagram and answer the question that follows.

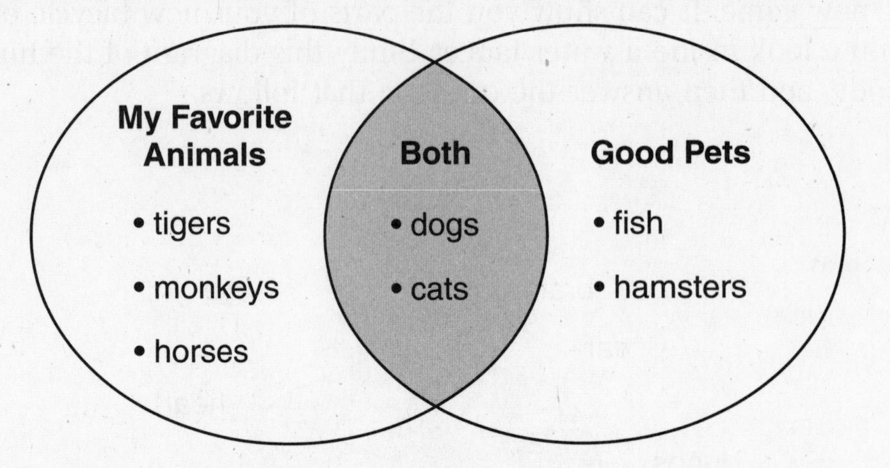

20. Which animals are among Carmelita's favorites, but would not make good pets?
    A. dogs
    B. cats
    C. fish
    D. tigers

TIP 8: Information about a subject can be grouped together and shown using webs.

Information can be clustered (grouped together) using ovals or circles and joining them together with lines to make something like a spider's **web.** Study this karate web and answer the question that follows.

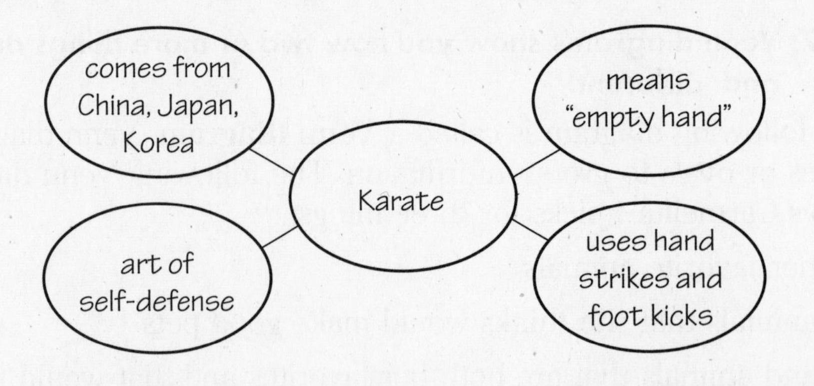

21. According to the web, what does the word karate mean?
    A. foot kicks
    B. self-defense
    C. hand strike
    D. empty hand

Reading Pictures

Lesson 14 Summary

When answering questions about graphs, charts or tables, diagrams, and webs, remember the following tips:

- Picture graphs show information with pictures.
- Circle graphs show parts of a whole.
- Bar graphs compare different amounts of the same kinds of things.
- Line graphs show changes over time.
- Charts (or tables) are used to show numbers in a way that is easy to read and understand.
- Flow charts and diagrams help you see how things work, how events happen, or how parts are put together.
- Venn diagrams show you how two or more things are alike and different.
- Information about a subject can be grouped together and shown using webs.

CRCT Practice

Directions: Look at the charts and diagrams, and then answer the questions.

Mrs. Hernandez took her third grade class on a field trip to Zoo Atlanta. The following day, she asked her students which animals were their favorite. Then she put the information into a fancy pie chart like this one.

Favorite Animals

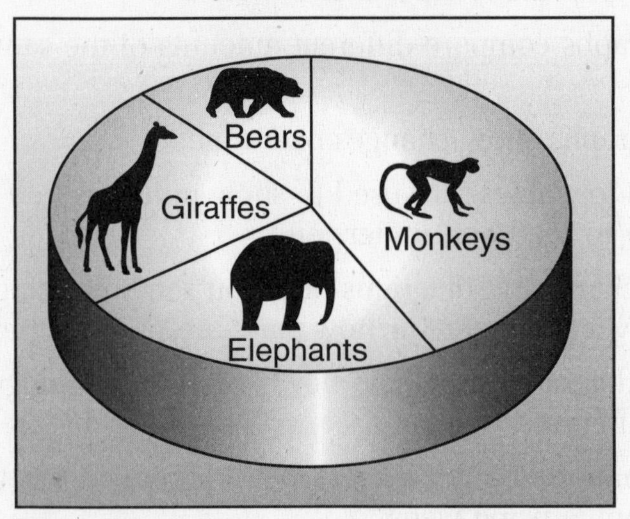

1. **What was the favorite animal of most students?**

   A. bears

   B. giraffes

   C. elephants

   D. monkeys

2. **What was the LEAST favorite animal of the students?**

   A. bears

   B. giraffes

   C. elephants

   D. monkeys

Mrs. Chong teaches 3rd Grade at Nicholls Elementary School on Atlantic Avenue in Waycross, Georgia. She asked her students how they got to school. Then she put the information into a bar graph.

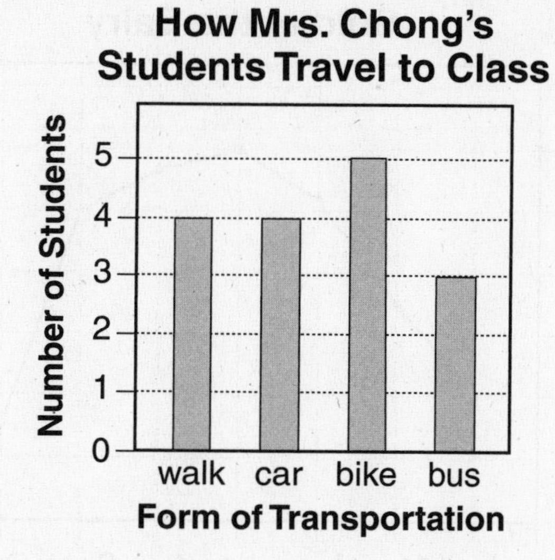

3. How do MOST students get to school?

A. walk

B. car

C. bike

D. bus

4. How do the FEWEST number of students get to school?

A. walk

B. car

C. bike

D. bus

Mr. Phillips owns a dairy store. He made this line graph to show how much chocolate ice cream he sold from April through October.

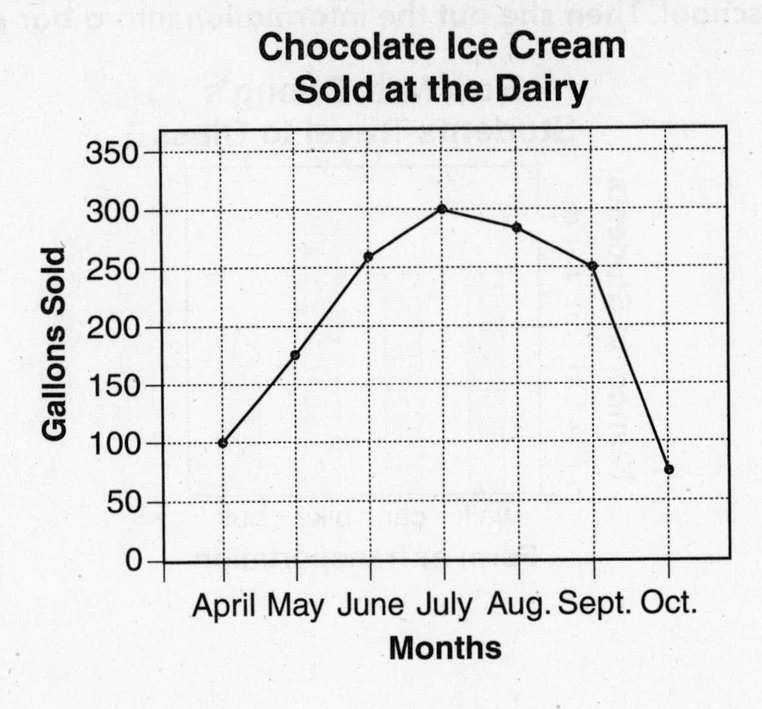

5. During which month did the dairy sell the MOST chocolate ice cream?

A. June

B. July

C. August

D. September

6. How many gallons of chocolate ice cream did the dairy sell in September?

A. 100

B. 180

C. 250

D. 300

Blue Route City Bus Schedule

Stop	Bus 1 Arrival Time	Bus 2 Arrival Time	Bus 3 Arrival Time
Westdale Mall	8:05 A.M.	8:40 A.M.	9:15 A.M.
City Library	8:13 A.M.	8:48 A.M.	9:23 A.M.
Fulton Stadium	8:25 A.M.	9:00 A.M.	9:35 A.M.
Osgood Park	8:34 A.M.	9:09 A.M.	9:44 A.M.
Train Station	8:43 A.M.	9:18 A.M.	9:53 A.M.

7. If Lucy takes Bus 1 from Westdale Mall at 8:05 A.M., what time will she get to Osgood Park?

A. 8:13 A.M.

B. 8:25 A.M.

C. 8:34 A.M.

D. 8:43 A.M.

8. If Daniel takes Bus 3 from the City Library at 9:23 A.M., what time will he get to Fulton Stadium?

A. 9:15 A.M.

B. 9:35 A.M.

C. 9:44 A.M.

D. 9:53 A.M.

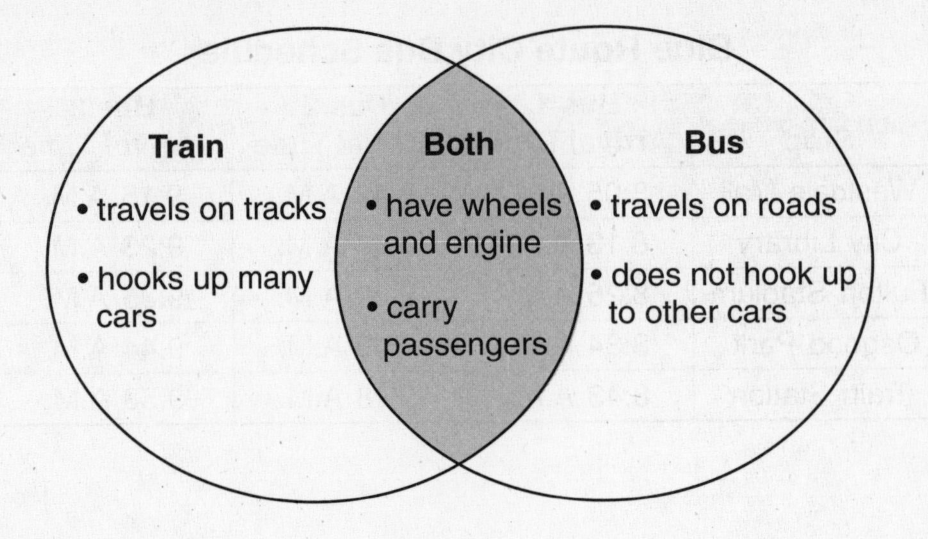

9. Which of the following is true of BOTH trains and buses?

A. They travel on tracks.

B. They travel on roads.

C. They hook up many cars.

D. They carry passengers.

Additional Practice Questions

10. Which suffix can you add to the end of the word *hard* to make it mean *most hard*?

A. -ly

B. -est

C. -er

D. -en

11. Which two words rhyme?

A. dive, did

B. hall, heel

C. glue, shoe

D. safe, soft

Notes

Notes

Notes

Notes

Notes

Notes

Notes

Notes